Kindergarten

Treasures

Home-School
Connection

D1501395

McGraw Hill **Macmillan**
McGraw-Hill

Credits: page 317

The *McGraw·Hill* Companies

Macmillan
McGraw-Hill

Published by Macmillan/McGraw-Hill, of McGraw-Hill Education, a division of The McGraw-Hill
Companies, Inc., Two Penn Plaza, New York, New York 10121-2298.

Printed in the United States of America

4 5 6 7 8 9 045 10 09 08 07 06

Contents

Beginning of the Year Letter
in English and Spanish

▲ Decodable Readers   ● On-Level Books

▲ Decodable Readers   ● On-Level Books

Dear Family Member:

You can help your child practice reading skills taught at school. Working together you and your child can become partners in learning.

Each week your child will bring home:

- A **letter** that tells you about the book the class is reading that week

- Three **homework activities** that will improve reading skills and offer practice with words your child is learning

- One or two **stories** for the two of you to read together

Your interest, praise, and encouragement are sure to lead to your child's success.

Queridos familiares:

Con su ayuda, su niño/a puede practicar las destrezas de lectura aprendidas en la escuela. Este trabajo conjunto les permitirá ser compañeros de aprendizaje.

Cada semana, su niño/a va a llevar a casa lo siguiente:

- Una **carta** contándole acerca lo que ha leído en clase durante esa semana.

- Tres **actividades de tareas para el hogar** para mejorar las destrezas de lectura y practicar las palabras que está aprendiendo.

- También llevará a casa uno o dos **cuentos** para leer juntos.

Su interés, apoyo y estímulo guiarán a su niño/a al éxito.

Dear Family Member:

This week we are reading *Whose Baby Am I?* Every baby has parents. A baby owl is called an *owlet*. A baby elephant is a *calf*. I am learning how to guess what will happen next in a story. I use what I know. I use the pictures. Together I can make my guess.

This Week's Skills

Comprehension: make predictions

High-Frequency Word: We

Concept Words: size words

Phonics: m

Would you like to go on a treasure hunt? Look for words on containers in your kitchen that begin with the letter m.

Name _____

(Fold here)

© Macmillan/McGraw-Hill

Word Workout

Talk About It

VOCABULARY

animal   together

Name an animal you may have at home, in school, or in your neighborhood. What fun could you have with the animal?

MY WORDS TO KNOW

High-Frequency Word: We

I'm going to write the word *we* on a piece of paper and read it to you. You can trace the word on my back as you say the letters. Then we can make up sentences together that begin *We can* _____.

Concept Words: size words

big, small, short, tall

Name a pair of animals, such as a mouse and an elephant. Which one is **big**? Which one is **small**? Which one is **short**? Which one is **tall**? Let's do the same thing with other kinds of animals or objects.

What's Next?

Let's talk about what is happening in each big picture and in the two smaller ones next to it. Draw a box around the small picture that shows what will happen next. Tell me your reason for choosing the picture you put in a box.

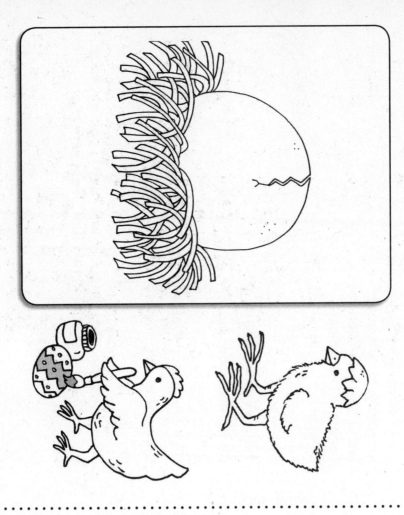

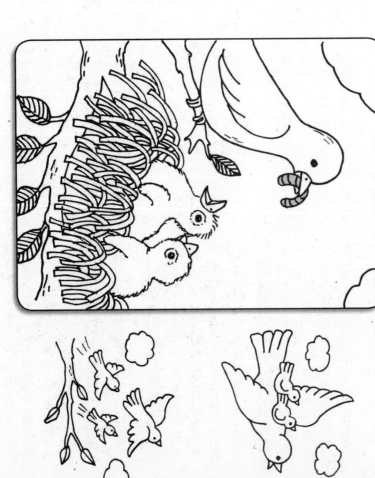

Queridos familiares:

Esta semana estamos leyendo *Whose Baby Am I?* Todos los bebés tienen padres. En inglés el bebé de una lechuza se llama *owlet* y el bebé de un elefante se llama *calf*. Estoy aprendiendo a adivinar lo que pasará después en un cuento. Uso lo que sé y también las ilustraciones. Con esas dos cosas puedo ir adivinando.

MIS DESTREZAS DE LA SEMANA

Comprensión: hacer predicciones

Palabra de uso frecuente: We

Palabras de concepto: palabras que indican tamaño

Fonética: m

¿Te gustaría participar en una caza del tesoro? Busca palabras que empiecen con la letra m en recipientes de tu cocina.

Nombre _____

(fold here)

Ejercicio de palabras

Talk About it

VOCABULARIO

animal   together

Nombra un animal de tu casa, de la escuela o de tu vecindad. ¿Cómo podrías divertirte con ese animal?

MIS PALABRAS

Palabra de uso frecuente: We

Voy a escribir la palabra *we* en un papel y te la voy a leer. Traza la palabra sobre mi espalda a medida que vayas diciendo las letras. Entonces podemos hacer juntos oraciones que comiencen *We can _____*.

Palabras de concepto: palabras que indican tamaño

big, small, short, tall

¿Cuál es **small**? ¿Cuál es **short**? ¿Cuál es **tall**? Vamos a hacer lo mismo con otras clases de animales u objetos. Nombra un par de animales, como ratón y elefante. ¿Cuál es **big**?

¿Qué viene después?

Vamos a hablar de lo que está pasando en cada una de las ilustraciones grandes y en las dos más pequeñas que están al lado. Encierra en un recuadro la ilustración pequeña donde se ve lo que va a pasar después. Dime cuál es tu razón para escoger esa ilustración.

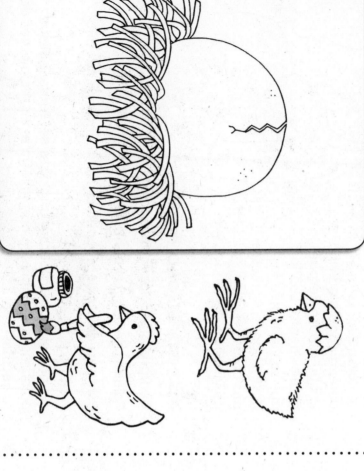

My Mitten

by Jack Benson

My Mitten

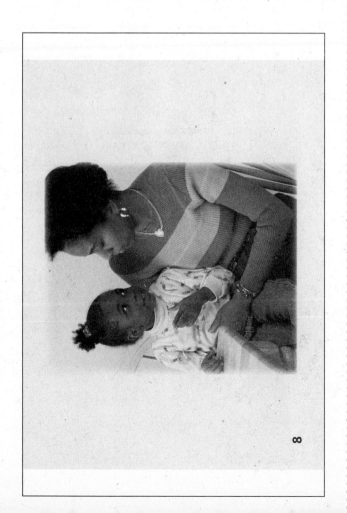

3

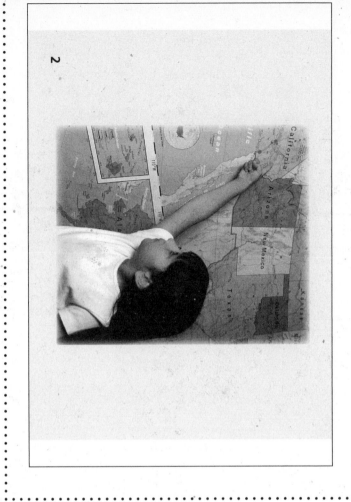

2

My Mitten

9

7

We Can

by Cynthia Swain

We can.

8

2

We can.

Monkeys can.

7

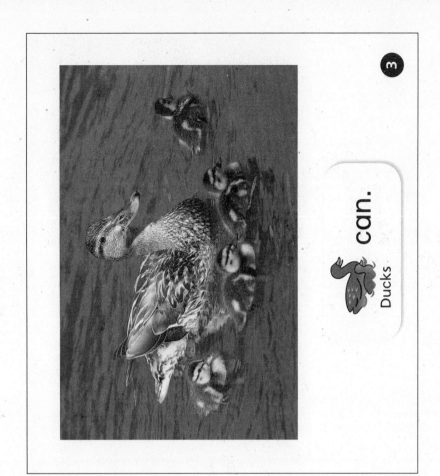

Ducks can.

We can.

4

We can.

Cats can.

5

Dear Family Member:

This week we are reading *The Picnic at Apple Park*. Families in a neighborhood pack up food and games for a picnic at the park. I am learning that stories can happen in different places and at different times. This is the *setting*. This story starts inside each family's home. Then, everyone is at the park.

This Week's Skills

Comprehension: identify setting

High-Frequency Word: the

Concept Words: size words

Phonics: a
Hunt for words with the letter a. Have your child point to the letter a in each word and name it.

(fold here)

© Macmillan/McGraw-Hill

Word Workout

Talk About it

VOCABULARY

activities cooperater

Talk about group activities that your child participates in. Discuss ways in which the group members cooperate.

MY WORDS TO KNOW

High-Frequency Word: the

Look for the word *the* in book titles, on signs, and in newspapers. You and your child can write the word in the air as you name the letters. Then have your child write *the* on a piece of paper.

Concept Words: size words

same, different

Play "Same or Different" with your child, using pairs of objects that are the same and different sizes, such as your shoes and your child's shoes, your hand and your child's hand, and so on.

Ask, for example: Are these hands the **same** or **different?** How are they the same and how are they different?

Name _____

Where Is It?

Who can get their dog home first? We need a coin and two small objects for markers. First, flip the coin. We'll take turns, moving one space for "heads" or two spaces for "tails." Move your coin and marker one space and describe the setting of the picture. Whoever gets their dog home first wins!

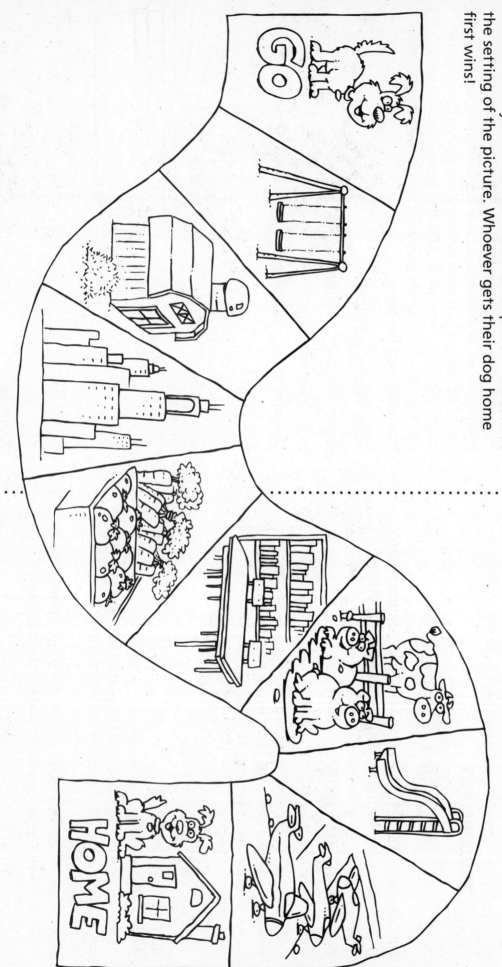

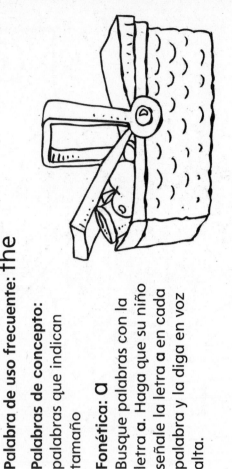

Queridos familiares:

Esta semana estamos leyendo *The Picnic at Apple Park*. Las familias de una vecindad empacan comida y juegos para ir de picnic al parque. Estoy aprendiendo que los cuentos pueden ocurrir en distintos lugares y en épocas diferentes. Eso se llama *ambiente*. Este cuento comienza en la casa de cada familia. Luego se encuentran todos en el parque.

MIS DESTREZAS DE LA SEMANA

Comprensión: identificar el ambiente

Palabra de uso frecuente: the

Palabras de concepto: palabras que indican tamaño

Fonética: a
Busque palabras con la letra a. Haga que su niño señale la letra a en cada palabra y la diga en voz alta.

Nombre _____

(fold here)

© Macmillan/McGraw-Hill

Ejercicio de palabras

 Talk About it

VOCABULARIO

activities   cooperater

Platique acerca de actividades de grupo en las que su niño participe. Comente distintas formas en que cooperan los miembros del grupo.

MIS PALABRAS

Palabra de uso frecuente: the

Busque la palabra *the* en títulos de libros, en carteles y en los periódicos. Junto con su niño puede escribir la palabra en el aire e ir nombrando las letras. Luego haga que el niño escriba la palabra *the* en un papel.

Palabras de concepto: palabras que indican tamaño

same, different

Juegue a *"Same or Different"* con su niño, usando pares de objetos iguales pero de tamaños diferentes, como los zapatos del niño, su mano y la mano del niño, etc. Pregúntele *different:* ¿Son nuestras manos iguales *(same)* o diferentes *(different)*? ¿En qué son iguales *(same)*? ¿En qué son diferentes *(different)*?

¿Dónde está?

¿Quién puede llevar primero su perro a la casa? Necesitamos una moneda y dos objetos pequeños que sirvan como marcadores. Primero vamos a tirar la moneda. Mueve un espacio si la moneda cae en *"heads"*. Describe el ambiente de la ilustración. Vamos a turnarnos y a mover un espacio para *heads* o dos para *tails*. Gana el que primero lleve su perro a la casa.

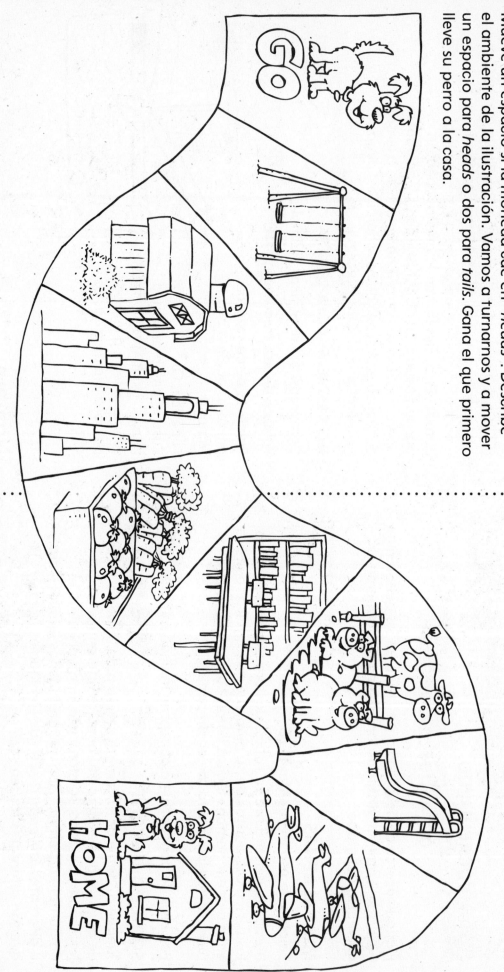

I Am Picking Apples

by Wiley Blevins
illustrated by Ann Iosa

4

I Am Picking Apples

5

8

I Am Picking Apples

3

2

6

7

Family Dinner

by Cal Ryan   illustrated by Diane Dawson Hearn

8

Family Dinner

I am the  dog .

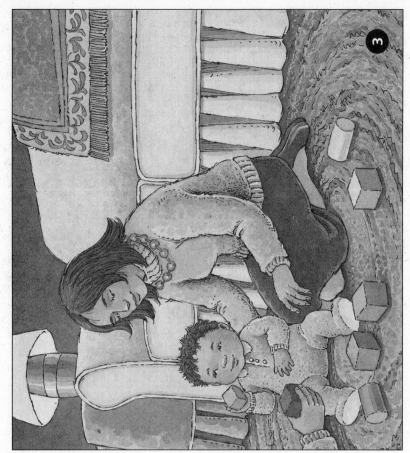

Family Dinner

3

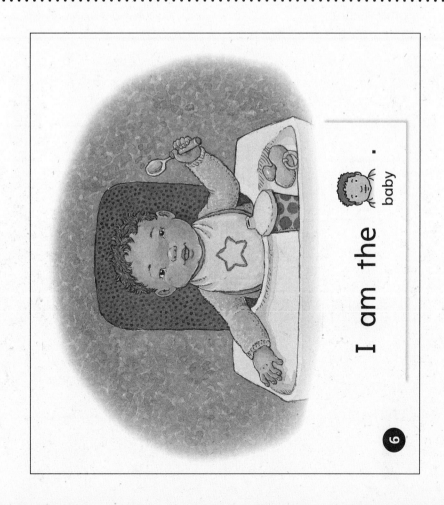

I am the .

baby

6

I am the  mom .

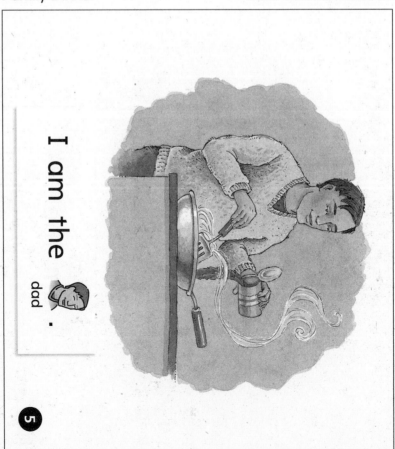

I am the dad .

Home-School Connection

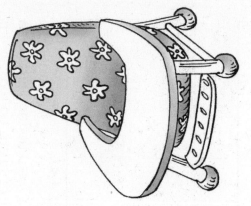

Dear Family Member:

This week we are reading *Peter* Peter has a new baby sister. His p have painted his old cradle for the baby, and they want to paint his old blue chair. He doesn't want them to paint his old blue chair! I am learning how to use the pictures and details in a book along with what I know from my life to guess what will happen next. We will be reading about what Peter does with his old chair.

This Week's Skills

Comprehension: make predictions

High-Frequency Words: we, the

Concept Words: size words

Phonics: review m, a

I'm going to trace a letter on your back. Then you can trace a letter on my back. I'll trace the letters you are studying this week.

Name _____

·····(fold here)·····

Word Workout

 Talk About it

VOCABULARY

change   relatives

Name some of our relatives. How do we think relatives change as they grow up and get older?

MY WORDS TO KNOW

High-Frequency Words: we, the

I'm going to write each word on a sticky note and put them on the table. Then I'll say the words and you can point to each one. Then we can say the word. We can look for these words in some of your books. Stick each note on the page where you find the word.

Concept Words: size words

big, small, short, tall

Let's play "Who Is It?" I'll ask questions about our relatives. For example: Who is **big**? Who is **short**? You can answer the questions.

What Will Happen?

Let's talk about what's happening in the pictures on the left. What do you think will happen next? Draw a line from the picture on the left to the one on the right that shows what will happen next. Tell me how you chose each pair of pictures.

We can play the same game on this page.

Queridos familiares:

Esta semana estamos leyendo *Pe Chair.* Peter tiene una hermanita nu Sus papás han pintado la vieja cunc de Peter para el bebé, y también quieren pintar su vieja silla azul. ¡Peter no quiere que pinten su silla! Estoy aprendiendo a usar las ilustraciones y los detalles de un libro, junto con lo que sé por mi experiencia, para adivinar qué pasará después. Vamos a leer sobre lo que hace Peter con su silla vieja.

MIS DESTREZAS DE LA SEMANA

Comprensión: hacer predicciones

Palabras de uso frecuente: we, the

Palabras de concepto: palabras que indican tamaño

Fonética: repaso de la m y la a
Voy a trazar una letra sobre tu espalda. Después tú puedes trazar una sobre la mía. Voy a trazar las letras que tú estás estudiando esta semana.

Nombre _____

(Fold here.)

Ejercicio de palabras

VOCABULARIO

change   relatives

Nombra a alguno de nuestros parientes. ¿Cómo piensas que los parientes cambian cuando crecen y se vuelven mayores?

MIS PALABRAS

Palabras de uso frecuente: we, the

Voy a escribir cada una de estas palabras en una nota adhesiva y ponerlas todas sobre la mesa. Voy a decir cada palabra y tú debes señalarla. Luego vamos a decir juntos la palabra. Podemos buscar estas palabras en tus libros. Pega la nota adhesiva en la página donde veas la palabra.

Palabras de concepto: palabras que indican tamaño

big, small, short, tall

Vamos a jugar a "¿Quién es?". Te voy a hacer preguntas sobre nuestros parientes, por ejemplo: ¿Quién es **big**? ¿Quién es **short**? Tú debes contestar las preguntas.

¿Qué va a pasar?

Vamos a hablar sobre lo que pasa en las ilustraciones de la izquierda. ¿Qué te parece que va a pasar después? Traza una línea de la ilustración de la izquierda a la de la derecha que muestra lo que va a pasar. Dime por qué escogiste cada par de ilustraciones.

Jugemos el mismo juego aquí.

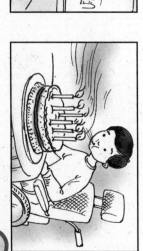

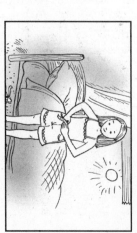

I Am in My Attic

by Amy Helfer

illustrated by Nathan Jarvis

4

I Am in My Attic

5

8

3

2

I Am in My Attic

6

7

I Grow Up

by Katie Ungaro   illustrated by John Nez

We 🥣 the 🥣.

eat   soup

8

2

I am 1.

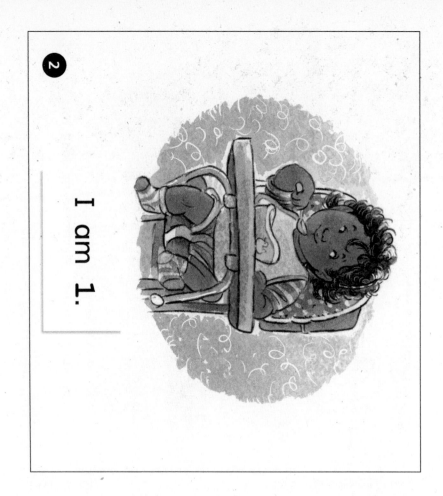

I Grow Up

We  the 🥣 .

eat   soup

7

We 🥄 the 🥣.
eat   soup

I Grow Up

3

I am 16.

6

I am 8.

4

I Grow Up

We  the  .

eat   soup

5

Home-School Connection

Dear Family Member:

This week we are reading *What Do You Like?* A girl likes the rainbow. So does a boy. They both like to play. I'm learning about characters in a story. The characters in this book are the girl and boy. I can learn about characters by what they do and say or what the writer says about them.

This Week's Skills

Comprehension: identify character

High-Frequency Word: like

Concept Words: color words

Phonics: S

I'm going to hunt for words that start with the letter s, and I'll read each word. Then you can think of other words that begin with the same sound.

Name _____

(fold here)

Word Workout

Talk About It

VOCABULARY

favorite   friendship

Who is a good friend? You have a friendship with that child. Tell me your favorite things about your friend.

MY WORDS TO KNOW

High-Frequency Word: like

Let's make a list of things you like. On a piece of paper, I'll write sentences that begin *I like* _____. Then we can read the list together. You can point to the word *like* in each sentence as we read together.

Concept Words:

red yellow blue

We're going to play "Same or Different" using things that are the same and different sizes. For example: Are these pencils the **same** or **different**? How? Let's name other people or objects we can compare.

Let's play "Color me." I'll point out things in our home, and you can tell me if they are **red, yellow, or blue.**

All About Who?

Let's choose two characters. You can you draw a picture of one, and I'll draw the other one. For example, we might draw "Red Riding Hood" carrying her basket of food. We might draw the "Big Bad Wolf" knocking on the grandmother's door. Then we can ask each other questions such as: *What does your character look like? How does your character act? What are some things your character does?*

Queridos familiares:

Esta semana estamos leyendo *What Do You Like?* A una niña le gusta el arco iris. También le gusta a un niño. A los dos les gusta jugar. Estoy aprendiendo acerca de los personajes de un cuento. Los personajes de este libro son el niño y la niña. Puedo aprender sobre los personajes por lo que dicen y hacen, o por lo que dice el autor acerca de ellos.

MIS DESTREZAS DE LA SEMANA

Comprensión: identificar personajes

Palabra de uso frecuente: like

Palabras de concepto: palabras que indican color

Fonética: S

Voy a buscar palabras que comiencen con la letra s y voy a leer cada palabra. Luego tú puedes pensar en otras palabras que comiencen con el mismo sonido.

Nombre _____

(fold here)

© Macmillan/McGraw-Hill

Ejercicio de palabras

Talk About it

VOCABULARIO

favorite   friendship

¿Quién es tu amigo o amiga favorito? Lo que sientes por él o por ella se llama amistad. Dime las cosas que te gustan más de tu amigo o amiga favorito

MIS PALABRAS

Palabra de uso frecuente: like

Vamos a hacer una lista de las cosas que te gustan. En una hoja de papel voy a escribir oraciones que comiencen *I like* _____. Después vamos a leer juntos la lista y tú vas a señalar la palabra like en cada oración que leamos.

Palabras de concepto:

red yellow blue

Vamos a jugar a "colorear". Voy a señalar cosas de nuestra casa y tú me dirás se son de color *red, yellow o blue.*

¿Acerca de quién?

Vamos a escoger dos personajes. Tú puedes hacer la ilustración de uno y yo haré la del otro. Por ejemplo, podríamos dibujar a Caperucita Roja con una cesta de comida y al Lobo Feroz golpeando en la puerta de la abuela. Luego nos podemos preguntar: *¿Qué aspecto tiene tu personaje? ¿Cómo actúa? ¿Cuáles son algunas de las cosas que hace?*

We Like Sam!

by Stan Casey

4

We like the 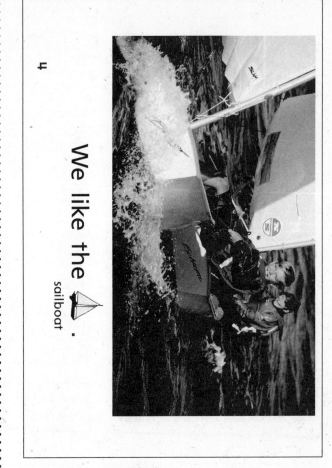 .

sailboat

We like Sam!

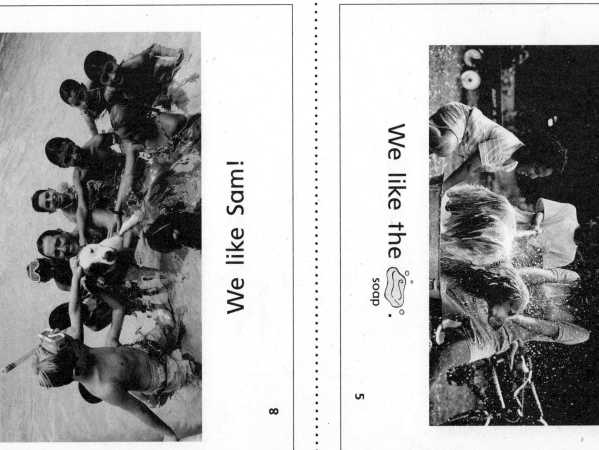

8

We like the .

soap

5

3

We like the  sand .

2

We like the ☀ sun .

We Like Sam!

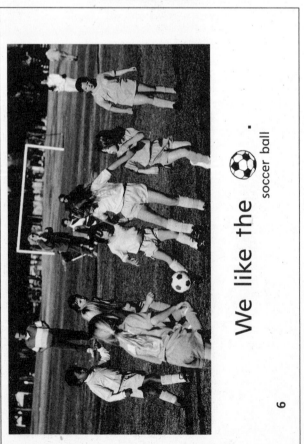

6

We like the ⚽ soccer ball .

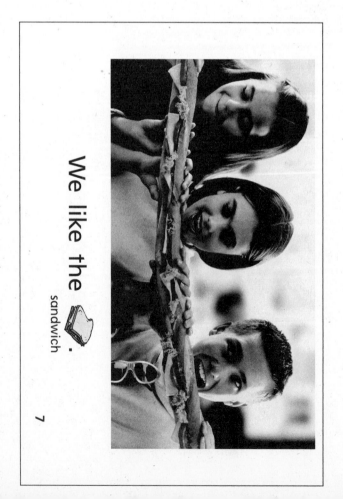

7

We like the sandwich .

We Like the Playground

by James Gee   illustrated by Rick Brown

We Like the Playground

We like the ___ playground .

8

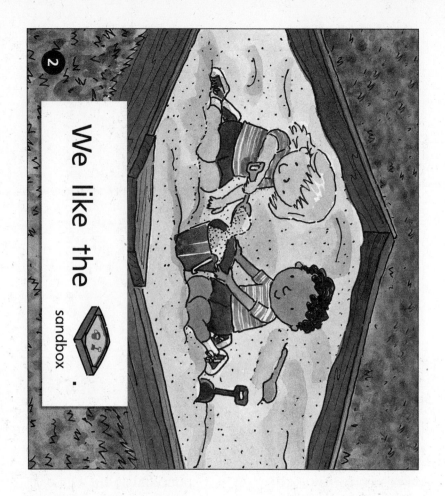

We like the

sandbox
.

2

We Like the Playground   © 2007 Macmillan/McGraw-Hill

We like the

sprinkler
.

7

We like the _____ .

merry-go-round

We Like the Playground

We like the _____ .

sand castle

We like the  .

swings

4

We Like the Playground

We like the .

slide

5

Dear Family Member:

This week we are reading *Friends All Around.* Friends can be alike or different. Some play fast music. Some play slow music. Friends can be different ages. I am learning how people in a book are alike and how they are different.

This Week's Skills

Comprehension: compare and contrast

High-Frequency Word: a

Concept Words: number words

Phonics: p

Let's find things at home that begin with the sound we hear at the beginning of the word *paint.* For each correct word, you can paint the letter **p** on a piece of paper.

Name _____

(fold here)

© Macmillan/McGraw-Hill

Word Workout

Talk About It

VOCABULARY

world   games

What games do you like to play? Do you think these games or other games you know are played in different parts of the world?

MY WORDS TO KNOW

High-Frequency Word: a

Let's look for the word a in books, on signs, and in other kinds of print. Point to the word and read the word each time you see it.

Concept Words:

one, two, three

Have you ever played "How Many"? I'm going to write **one, two,** and **three** on index cards. When I point to a card, count out that number of coins. Then write the word **one, two,** or **three** on each card. I'll help you.

47

Time for Lunch

Let's look at the two lunch boxes on this page and talk about what is inside each one.

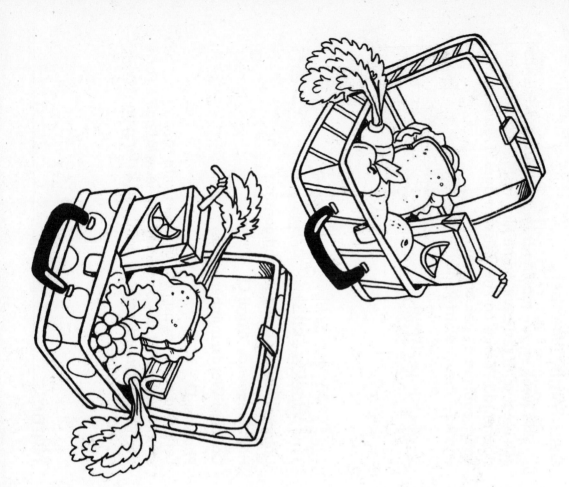

Now we can put a √ under each lunch box if the item is there.

Next we can put a √ next to any item in both lunch boxes.

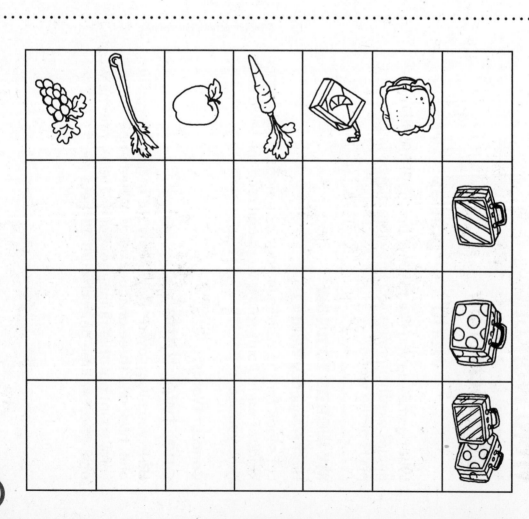

Queridos familiares:

Esta semana estamos leyendo *Friends All Around*. Los amigos pueden ser parecidos o diferentes. Algunos tocan música rápida; otros tocan música lenta. Los amigos pueden ser de distintas edades. Estoy aprendiendo en qué se parecen y se diferencian los personajes de un libro.

MIS DESTREZAS DE LA SEMANA

Comprensión: comparar y contrastar

Palabra de uso frecuente: a

Palabras de concepto: palabras que indican número

Fonética: p
Vamos a buscar en casa palabras que empiecen con el mismo sonido que escuchamos al comienzo de la palabra *paint*. Cada vez que encuentres una palabra vas a pintar la letra p en una hoja de papel.

Nombre _____

····· (fold here) ·····

© Macmillan/McGraw-Hill

Ejercicio de palabras

VOCABULARIO

Talk About it

world   games

¿A qué te gusta jugar? ¿Crees que los juegos que te gustan u otros juegos que conoces se juegan en diferentes partes del mundo?

MIS PALABRAS

Palabra de uso frecuente: a

Vamos a buscar la letra a en libros, en carteles y en otros tipos de impresos. Señala la palabra y léela cada vez que la veas.

Palabras de concepto:
one, two, three

¿Has jugado a *"How Many"* alguna vez? Voy a escribir *one, two* y *three* en tarjetas. Cuando yo señale una tarjeta, cuenta el mismo número en monedas. Luego escribe la palabra *one, two* o *three* en cada tarjeta. Yo te ayudaré.

49

¡Hora de almorzar!

Vamos a mirar las dos loncheras de esta página y platicar sobre lo que hay en cada una.

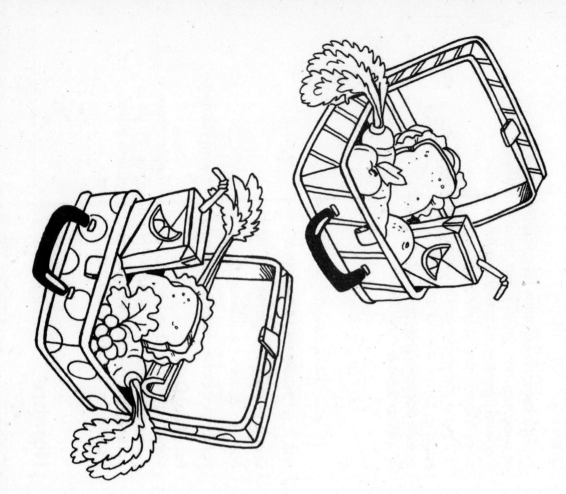

Now we can put a √ under each lunch box if the item is there.

Next we can put a √ next to any item in both lunch boxes.

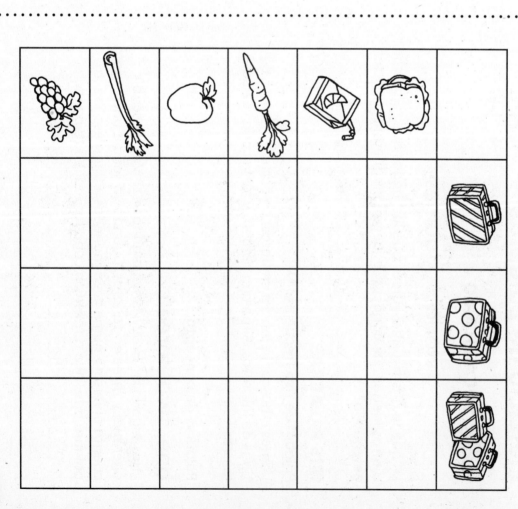

A Map

by Jeff Stanley

illustrated by Jared Lee

We like a .

pumpkin

We like the map!

We like a .

sheep

We like a map.

We like a  .

pig

A Map

We like a  .

pup

We like a 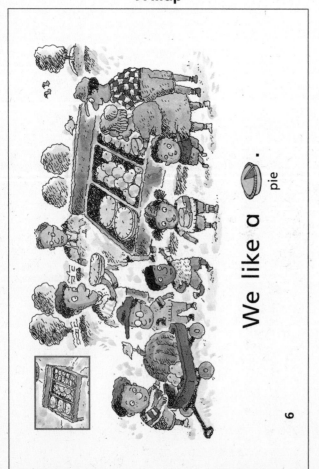 .

pie

We Can Share

by Carol Dale

We like a 🍕 .
pizza

8

We like a  . pear

2

We Can Share

We like a . pretzel

7

We like a  pie .

We like a pineapple .

4

© 2007 Macmillan/McGraw-Hill

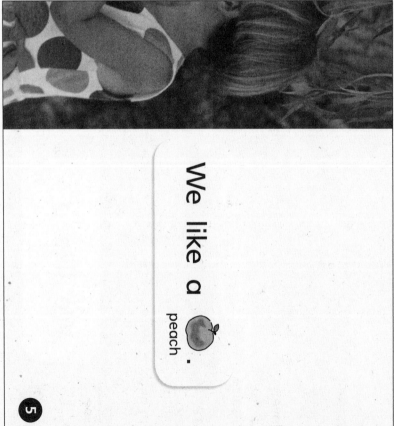

We like a .

peach

5

Dear Family Member:

This week we are reading *Simon and Molly Plus Hester*. Molly and Simon are best friends. They ride a bike. They make toast. Then Hester moves in. When Molly plays with Hester, Simon feels sad. I'm learning about characte by what they say and do The writer also tells us about them.

This Week's Skills

Comprehension: identif

High-Frequency Words: a, like

Concept Words: color words

Phonics: s, p
We can hunt for words that begin with the letters s and p in books we are reading together.

······· (Fold here) ·······

Word Workout

 Talk About It

VOCABULARY

solve   problem

Have your child talk about a problem that might come up when they are playing with friends. What are some ways to solve the problem?

MY WORDS TO KNOW

High-Frequency Words: a, like

I'm going to write each word on a card and read them with you. Tell me the word that goes in each sentence:
I ____ you; I would ____ a pet; ____ giant is big.
I see ____ book.

Concept Words: color words

yellow, red, blue, purple, green

Let's play "Match It." I'll write the colors **yellow, red, blue, purple,** and **green** across the top of a piece of paper. I'll cut pieces of colored paper, and you can match the piece to the correct color.

Name _____

Who Am I?

I'm going to ask you some riddles. Can you guess which character I'm talking about? Draw a line between the riddle and the character.

I am smart. I built my house of bricks. Who am I?

I like to walk in the woods. I carry a basket. Who am I?

I can be very scary. Who am I?

I am going to marry a prince? Who am I?

Conexión con el hogar

Queridos familiares:

Esta semana estamos leyendo *Simon and Molly Plus Hester*. Simon y Molly son muy buenos amigos. Ellos montan en bicicleta. También hacen tostadas.

Después Hester se muda a la vecindad. Cuando Molly juega con Hester, Simon se pone triste. Aprendo acerca de los personajes a través de lo que hacen y dicen. El escritor también nos cuenta cosas sobre ellos.

MIS DESTREZAS DE LA SEI

Comprensión: identificar a los personajes

Palabras de uso frecuente: a, like

Palabras de concepto: palabras que indican color

Fonética: s, p

Vamos a buscar palabras que empiecen con la letra **s** o con la letra **p** en los libros que estamos leyendo juntos.

Nombre _____

·········· (Fold here) ··········

© Macmillan/McGraw-Hill

Ejercicio de palabras

Talk About It

VOCABULARIO

solve   problem

Haga que su niño hable de un problema que puede tener cuando juega con sus amigos. ¿De qué manera se puede resolver el problema?

MIS PALABRAS

Palabras de uso frecuente: a, like

Voy a escribir cada palabra en una tarjeta y leerla contigo. Dime la palabra que debe ir en cada oración.

I ____ you; I would ____ a pet; ____ giant is big.

I see ____ book.

Palabras de concepto: palabras que indican color

yellow, red, blue, purple, green

Vamos a jugar *"Match It"*. Voy a escribir los colores **yellow, red, blue, purple** y **green** en la parte de arriba de una hoja. Voy a cortar hojas de papel colorado y puedes emparejar la hoja al color correcto.

59

¿Quién soy?

Te voy a hacer algunas adivinanzas. ¿Puedes adivinar de qué personaje estoy hablando? Traza una línea entre la adivinanza y el personaje.

I am smart. I built my house of bricks. Who am I?

I like to walk in the woods. I carry a basket. Who am I?

I can be very scary. Who am I?

I am going to marry a prince? Who am I?

Pam

by Amy Helfer
illustrated by Nathan Jarvis

Sam? Sam?

Pam

Sam!

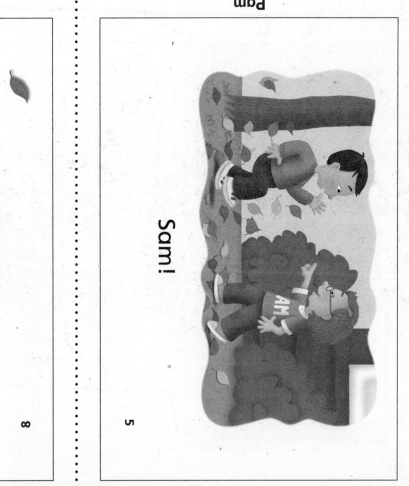

I like Pam.

I like Sam.

3

I am Pam.

2

Pam

Pam? Pam?

9

Pam!

7

We Like Painting

by Jane Hearn   illustrated by Noah Jones

We Like Painting

8

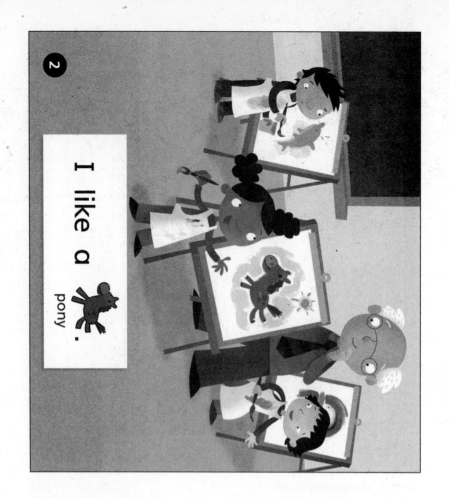

I like a  pony .

2

We Like Painting

I like a seahorse .

7

We Like Painting

3

I like a  seal .

6

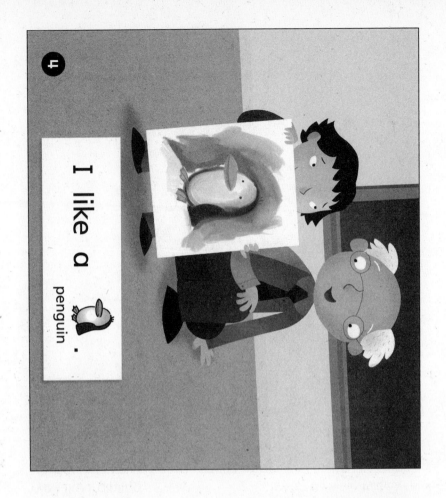

I like a . penguin

We Like Painting

I like a . porpoise

Dear Family Member:

This week we are reading *The Bus for Us*. Tess and Gus see a garbage truck, a backhoe, and other vehicles while they wait for the school bus. I am learning how to use the pictures and words in a book to guess what will happen next. I know we're going to see cars and trucks. I can tell because each page so far shows them.

This Week's Skills

Comprehension: make predictions

High-Frequency Word: See

Concept Words: shape words

Phonics: t
Let's hunt for words that start with the letter t. We can look in one of your books.

Name _____

······ (fold here) ······

© Macmillan/McGraw-Hill

Word Workout

VOCABULARY

transportation   vehicles

Name different kinds of vehicles you have ridden in, such as a bus, car, or train. Have you seen other kinds of transportation?

WORDS TO KNOW

High-Frequency Word: See

Look for the word see in signs, magazines, and newspapers. Have your child write see. Count the number of letters in the word.

Concept Words:

circle, triangle, square, rectangle

We can play "I Spy" using shape words. If I say: *I spy a red circle on the wall. What is it?* you would say: *the clock.* Let's play with more shape words.

What Will Happen Next?

Discuss what is happening in the first picture in each row. Ask: "What will happen next?" Have your child point to the picture at the right that shows what will happen next and explain her or his choice.

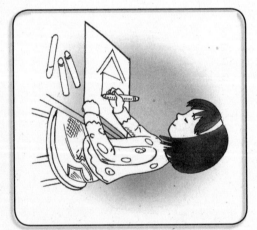

Queridos familiares:

Esta semana estamos leyendo *The Bus for Us*. Mientras esperan el autobús de la escuela Tess y Gus ven un camión de basura, una excavadora y otros vehículos. Estoy aprendiendo a usar las ilustraciones y las palabras de un libro para adivinar qué pasará después. Sé que vamos a ver autos y camiones. Lo sé porque hay autos y camiones en todas las páginas del libro que he visto hasta ahora.

MIS DESTREZAS DE LA SEMANA

Comprensión: hacer predicciones

Palabra de uso frecuente: see

Palabras de concepto: palabras que indican forma

Fonética: t
Vamos a buscar palabras que empiezan con la letra t. Podemos mirar en uno de tus libros.

Nombre _____

© Macmillan/McGraw-Hill

(Fold here.)

Ejercicio de palabras

Talk About it

VOCABULARIO

transportation   vehicles

¿En qué vehículos has andado? ¿Un autobús? ¿Un auto? ¿Un tren? ¿Haz visto otro tipo de transporte?

MIS PALABRAS

Palabra de uso frecuente: see

Busque la palabra see en carteles, revistas y periódicos. Pida a su niño que escriba see. Cuente el número de letras en la palabra.

Palabras de concepto: palabras que indican forma

circle, triangle, square, rectangle

Vamos a jugar a *"I Spy"* (Veo, veo) usando palabras que indican forma. Si te digo: *I spy a red circle on the wall. What is it?*, tú me contestarás: *the clock* (el reloj). Vamos a jugar con otras palabras que indican forma.

¿Qué pasará después?

Hable sobre lo que pasa en la primera ilustración de cada hilera. Pregunte: "¿Qué pasará después?" Haga que su niño señale la ilustración de la derecha que indica lo que sucederá después y que explique por qué ha escogido esa ilustración.

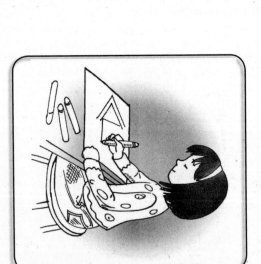

Can Tam See?

by Beverly Keis
Illustrated by Carol Schwartz

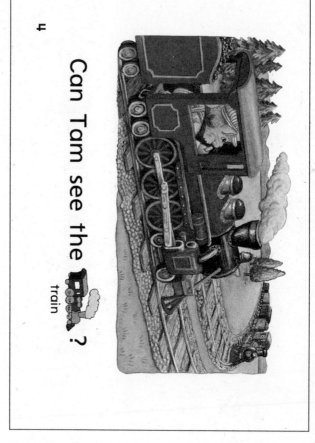

Can Tam see the train ?

4

Tam can see the train .

5

Tam can see Pat!

8

Tam can see the  boat .

3

Can Tam see the  boat ?

2

Can Tam See?

Can Tam see the jet ?

6

Tam can see the 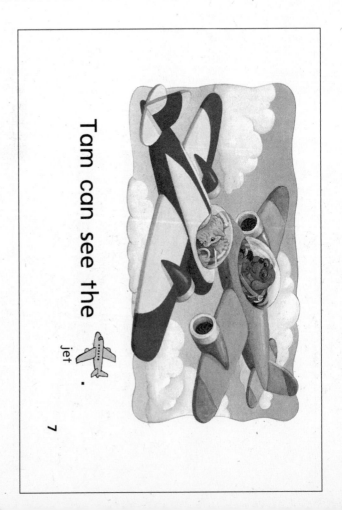 jet .

7

Tig Can See

by Jan Shen   illustrated by Jerry Smath

Tig can see the bird.

8

Tig can see the clock.

2

Tig can see the tree.

7

Tig Can See

Tig can see the 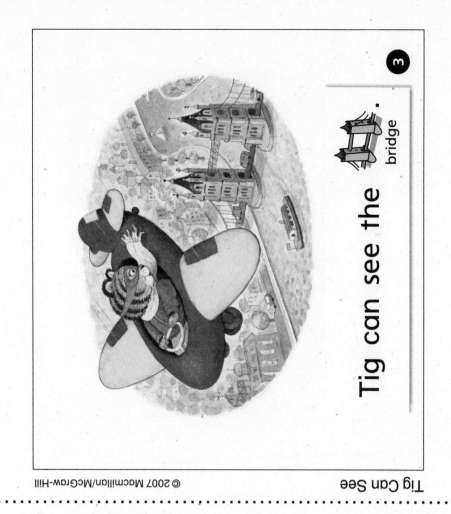 bridge .

3

Tig can see the boat .

6

4

Tig can see the

bus .

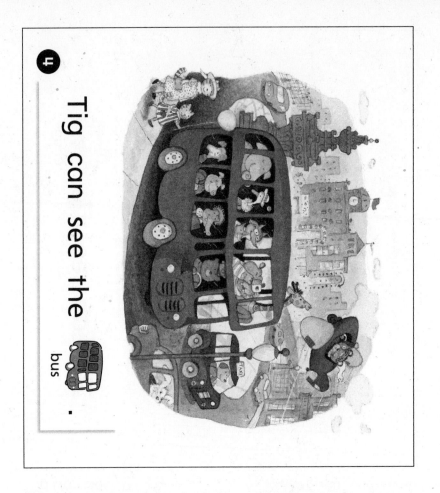

Tig Can See

© 2007 Macmillan/McGraw-Hill

Tig can see the cat .

5

Home-School Connection

Dear Family Member:

This week we are reading *On the Go*. I know that people all over the world go places. There are lots of ways to travel. I'm learning how to put things into groups. In this book, I can group things that move on wheels. Buses have wheels. So do trains, cars, and planes.

This Week's Skills

Comprehension: classify and categorize

High-Frequency Word: go

Concept Words: shape words

Phonics: i
This week when we read together, let's look for words that start with the letter i and have the letter i in them.

Name _____

(fold here)

© Macmillan/McGraw-Hill

Word Workout

VOCABULARY

Talk About it

travel   journey

Think of a place far away. Can we find it on a map? Let's talk about how you could travel there.

MY WORDS TO KNOW

High-Frequency Word: go

I'm writing the word go on a piece of paper. Trace it for me with a crayon. Now we'll use different colored crayons. Each time I say "Ready, set, go!" write **go** in a different color.

Concept Words:

oval, rectangle

I'm drawing two shapes. Their names are printed above. Can you name each shape I drew? We could add drawings to show the shapes of different kinds of transportation.

77

On the Move

Let's look at the pictures of the two trucks. What kinds of things do you think they carry? Draw a circle around any items the truck with vegetables might carry. Draw a square around items the truck with the chair might carry.

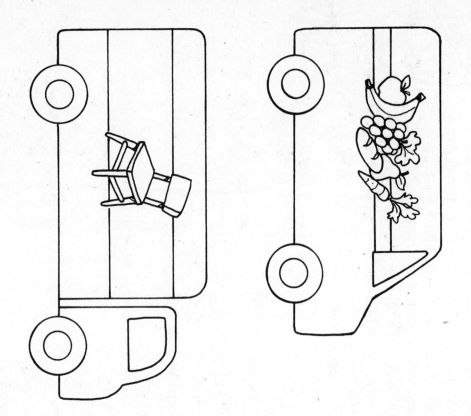

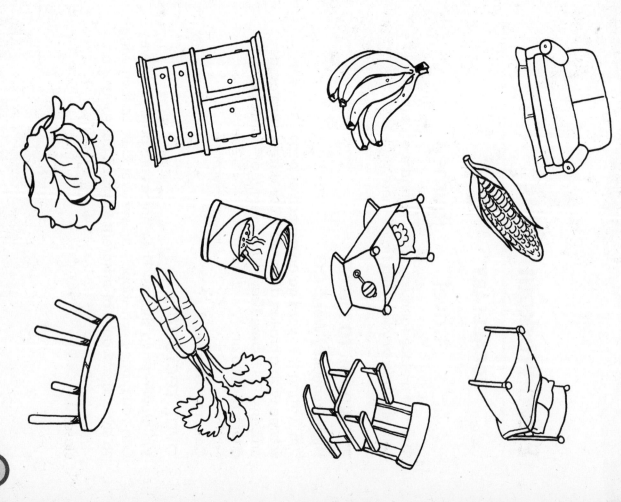

Conexión con el hogar

Queridos familiares:

Esta semana estamos leyendo *On the Go.* Sé que la gente de todo el mundo va a distintos lugares. Hay muchas maneras de viajar. Estoy aprendiendo a dividir las cosas en grupos. En este libro puedo agrupar cosas que se mueven sobre ruedas. Los autobuses tienen ruedas. También tienen ruedas los trenes, los autos y los aviones.

MIS DESTREZAS DE LA SEMANA

Comprensión: clasificar y categorizar

Palabra de uso frecuente: go

Palabras de concepto: palabras que indican forma

Fonética: i
Esta semana cuando leamos juntos vamos a buscar palabras que comiencen con i o que tengan la letra i.

Nombre _____

Ejercicio de palabras

 Talk About It

VOCABULARIO

travel   journey

Piensa en un lugar lejos de aquí. ¿Podemos encontrarlo en un mapa? Vamos a platicar sobre cómo podríamos viajar hasta ahí.

MIS PALABRAS

Palabra de uso frecuente: go

Estoy escribiendo la palabra *go* en un papel. Trázala con un creyón. Cuando termines usaremos creyones de colores diferentes. Cada vez que te diga: "¡Preparados, listos, ya!", escribe *go* con un color de creyón diferente.

Palabras de concepto:

oval, rectangle

Estoy dibujando dos formas. Los nombres están escritos arriba. ¿Puedes nombrar cada forma que dibujo? Podemos agregar dibujos para ilustrar las formas de diferentes clases de transporte.

¿Qué llevan?

Vamos a mirar las ilustraciones de los dos camiones. ¿Qué tipos de cosas crees que llevan? Encierra en un círculo lo que podría llevar el camión con los vegetales. Dibuja un cuadrado alrededor de lo que podría ir en el camión con la silla.

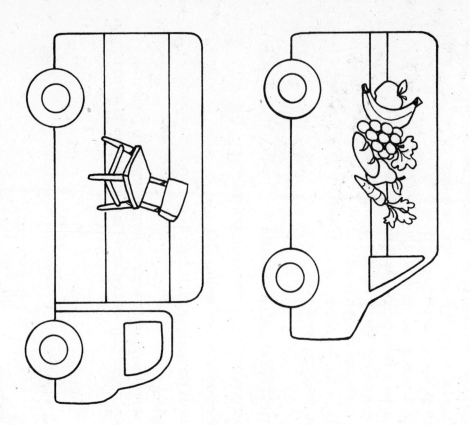

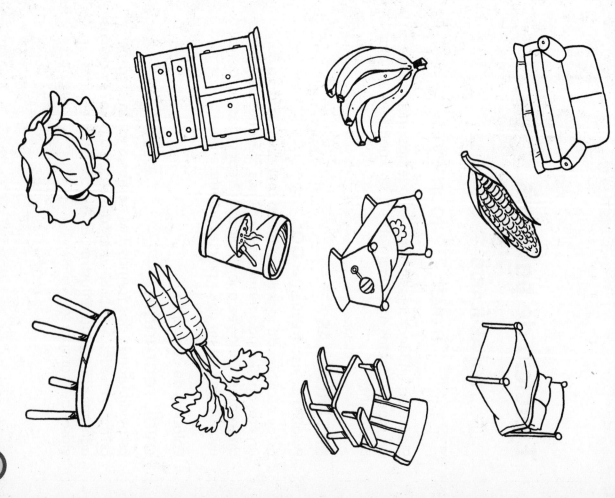

It Can Go, Go, Go!

by Michael LeRue

I can see a  .

boat

It Can Go, Go, Go!

It can go, go, go!

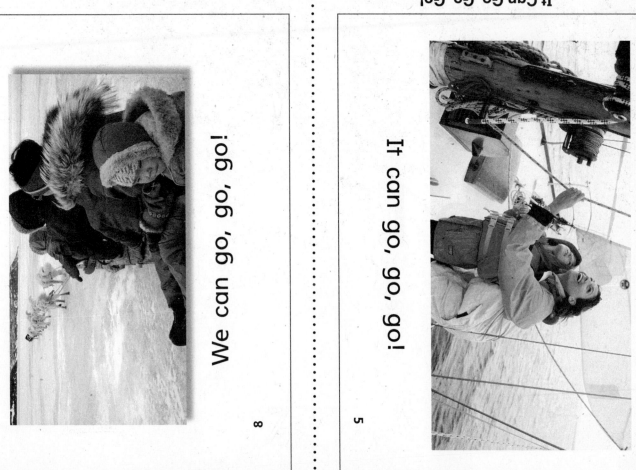

5

We can go, go, go!

8

It can go, go, go!

I like the 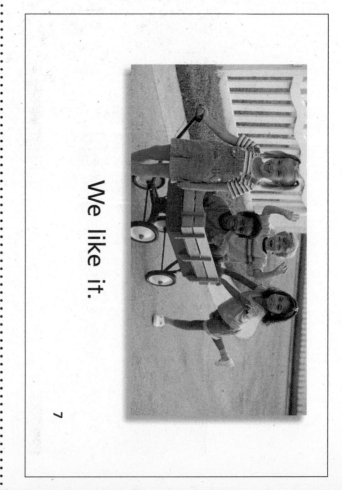.

car

It Can Go, Go, Go!

I see a 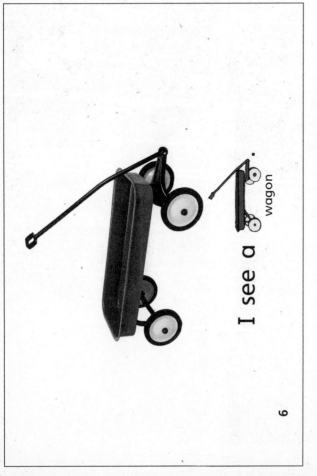.

wagon

We like it.

It can go fast.

8

Fast or Slow?

by Carrie Smith

2

It can go fast.

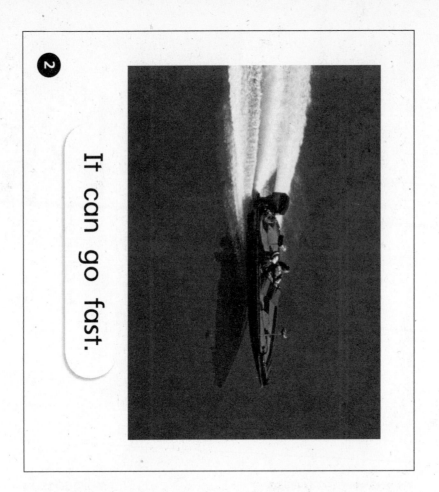

Fast or Slow? © 2007 Macmillan/McGraw-Hill

It can go slow.

7

It can go slow.

It can go fast.

6

4

It can go fast.

It can go slow.

5

Dear Family Member:

This week we are reading *Duck on a Bike*. Duck goes for a ride on a boy's bike. The cow thinks Duck is silly. The sheep thinks it could be dangerous. What will the other barnyard animals think? I'm learning about the characters in a story and the things that happen.

This Week's Skills

Comprehension: identify character and plot

High-Frequency Words: go, see, a, like

Concept Words: sound words

Phonics: t, i
Write the letters t and i in the space below.

Name _____

·····(fold here)······

Word Workout

Talk About It

VOCABULARY

adventure   wheels

Let's make up an adventure on wheels.

MY WORDS TO KNOW

High-Frequency Words: go, see, a, like

Tell me a sentence for each word. I'll print the sentences on a piece of paper and read them to you. Can you underline the words for this week?

Concept Words

meow, moo, quack, woof

Let's play "What Can I Say?" Here's a riddle for you: *I am a yellow duck on a pond. What can I say?* Answer the riddle with one of the words for this week. Now we can make more riddles.

Make Movies

We're going to make a movie. Let's talk about each drawing. Can you draw the missing ones? When we come to an empty frame you can draw what is missing.

Conexión con el hogar

Queridos familiares:

Esta semana estamos leyendo *Duck on a Bike*. El pato da un paseo en la bicicleta de un niño. La vaca piensa que el pato es gracioso. La oveja piensa que puede ser peligroso. ¿Qué pensarán los otros animales de la granja? Estoy aprendiendo sobre los personajes en un cuento y las cosas que les pasan. Ese es el argumento. Voy a ver cuáles son los otros personajes a medida que lea. Me pregunto qué pasará.

MIS DESTREZAS DE LA SEMANA

Comprensión: identificar personajes y argumento

Palabras de uso frecuente: go, see, a, like

Palabras de concepto: palabras que indican sonido

Fonética: t, i
Escribe en el espacio de abajo las letras t e i

Nombre _____

(fold here)

© Macmillan/McGraw-Hill

Ejercicio de palabras

Talk About it

VOCABULARIO

adventure   wheels

Inventemos de una aventura sobre ruedas.

MIS PALABRAS

Palabras de uso frecuente: go, see, a, like

Dime una oración con cada palabra. Yo escribiré las oraciones en una hoja de papel y te las leeré. ¿Puedes subrayar las palabras de la semana?

Palabras de concepto:

meow, moo, quack, woof

Vamos a jugar a "¿Qué digo yo?". Tengo una adivinanza para ti: *Soy un pato amarillo y estoy en una laguna. ¿Qué digo yo?* Contesta con una de las palabras de arriba. Ahora vamos a pensar en más adivinanzas.

89

¡Hagamos una película!

Vamos a hacer una película. Platiquemos acerca de cada ilustración. Cuando lleguemos a un recuadro vacío debes dibujar lo que falta.

Sit, Tip!

by Amy Helfer
illustrated by Nathan Jarvis

"I see Tip. Sit, Tip."

"We can go, Pam."

Tip sat. The 🧒 can go!

girls

8

"Can we go, Pat?"

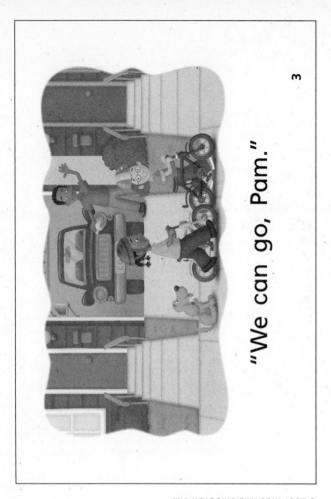

"We can go, Pam."

Sit, Tip!

"We can go."

"I see Tip. Sit, Tip."

Pig's Trip

by Sarah Newman   illustrated by Brian

Rays will be removed by separator

We see the 🐷 sit.

pig

8

We see the pig sit.

2

Pig's Trip

We see the pig go.

7

We see the  go.
pig

Pig's Trip

3

We see the go.
pig

We see the sit.
pig

6

4

We see the  sit.

pig

Pig's Trip

We see the pig go.

5

Dear Family Member:

This week we are reading *Apple Farmer Annie*. Annie has an apple tree orchard. She picks apples in the fall. Annie uses some of her apples to make different foods. She sells the best apples at a market in the city. I'm learning that the things that happen in a story, happen in a certain order. Remembering the order helps me understand a book. It helps me retell it, too.

This Week's Skills

Comprehension: identify sequence

High-Frequency Word: to

Concept Words: food words

Phonics: n

We can hunt for the letter n in a newspaper or a magazine. You can circle each n you find.

Name _____

·····································(fold here)·····································

© Macmillan/McGraw-Hill

Word Workout

Talk About It

VOCABULARY

farmer   market

Let's talk about things a farmer does. What things are in our local market thanks to farmers?

MY WORDS TO KNOW

High-Frequency Word: to

We can look for the word **to** in book titles, on signs, and in newspapers. Write the word in the air as you name the letters. Then write **to** on a piece of paper.

Concept Words: food words

tomato, beet, kiwi, peach

Let's draw pictures of different **fruits and vegetables.** When we are done, I'll shuffle the pictures and you can arrange them in two piles, one for **fruits** and the other for **vegetables.**

Farmer Fred's Day

Here's a puzzle we can solve. Draw a line to each place Farmer Fred goes.

First, he milked the cows. Next, he fed the chickens. Then he rode the tractor. Last, he brushed the horses. Farmer Fred went home for lunch.

Where did Farmer Fred go first?

What did he do second?

What did he do next?

Then what did he do?

Where did he end?

START

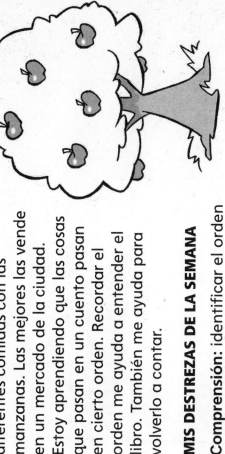

Conexión con el hogar

Queridos familiares:

Esta semana estamos leyendo *Apple Farmer Annie*. Annie tiene una huerta de manzanos. Ella recoge manzanas en el otoño. Annie prepara diferentes comidas con las manzanas. Las mejores las vende en un mercado de la ciudad. Estoy aprendiendo que las cosas que pasan en un cuento pasan en cierto orden. Recordar el orden me ayuda a entender el libro. También me ayuda para volverlo a contar.

MIS DESTREZAS DE LA SEMANA

Comprensión: identificar el orden de los sucesos

Palabra de uso frecuente: to

Palabras de concepto: palabras de comida

Fonética: n
Vamos a buscar la letra n en en un periódico o revista. Encierra cada n que encuentres en un círculo.

Nombre _____

· · · · · · · · · · · (fold here) · · · · · · · · · · ·

© Macmillan/McGraw-Hill

Ejercicio de palabras

 Talk About it

VOCABULARIO

farmer   market

Vamos a platicar sobre las cosas que hace un granjero. ¿Qué podemos encontrar en el mercado gracias a los granjeros?

MIS PALABRAS

Palabra de uso frecuente: to

Podemos buscar la palabra *to* en títulos de libros, carteles y periódicos. Escribe la palabra en el aire y nombra las letras. Luego escribe *to* en un papel.

Palabras de concepto: palabras de comida

tomato, beet, kiwi, peach

Vamos a dibujar **fruits and vegetables** diferentes. Cuando terminamos, voy a barajar los dibujos y puedes ponerlos en dos grupos, un para **fruits** y el otro para **vegetables**.

El día del granjero Fred

Aquí tenemos un rompecabezas para resolver. Traza una línea a cada lugar donde va el granjero Fred.

First, he milked the cows. Next, he fed the chickens. Then he rode the tractor. Last, he brushed the horses. Farmer Fred went home for lunch.

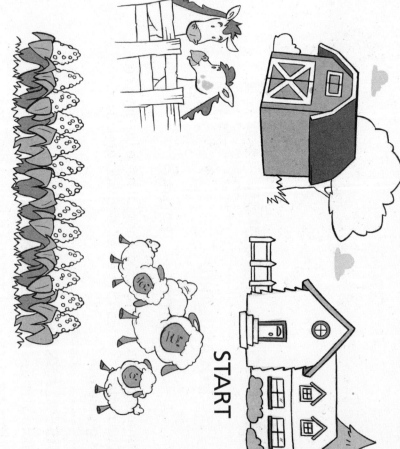

Where did Farmer Fred go first?

What did he do second?

What did he do next?

Then what did he do?

Where did he end?

START

Tap It, Nan Min!

by Toshio Ushida

photographed by Ken O'Donoghue

Pat, pat an  , Nan Min.

apple

4

Go to see Nat, Nan Min!

8

Tap, tap an  , Nan Min.

orange

5

Can Nan Min see Nat?

3

Go to the , Nan Min.

store

Tap It, Nan Min!

Tap, tap an , Nan Min.

onion

6

Pat, pat a 🥔, Nan Min.

potato

7

We Pick Food!

by Juana Rivera

We eat food!

8

2

We pick beans to eat.

We Pick Food!

We pick bananas to eat.

7

We pick nuts to eat.

We pick oranges to eat.

4

We Pick Food! © 2007 Macmillan/McGraw-Hill

We pick corn to eat.

5

Dear Family Member:

This week we are reading *Our Special Sweet Potato Pie.* A boy and his family want to make a sweet potato pie for Daddy's birthday. But the potatoes they pick start to roll down a hill. Everyone in the neighborhood tries to catch them. I'm learning that I can use story clues, picture clues, and what I already know to figure out things the writer doesn't say. I can tell from a picture in the books that Mr. Mason owns the bakery.

This Week's Skills

Comprehension: make inferences

High-Frequency Word: have

Concept Words: seasons

Phonics: C

You can use raisins or other small objects to form the letter c. Then we can hunt for words that start with the letter c in one of your books.

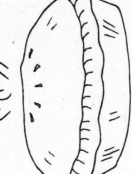

(fold here)

© Macmillan/McGraw-Hill

Name _____

Word Workout

Talk About it

VOCABULARY

special   feast

When do we celebrate holidays? Do we have a family feast? What makes it special?

MY WORDS TO KNOW

High-Frequency Word: have

Can you write the word have on a card? Then say sentences that begin *I have _____*. For example: *I have a coat.*

Concept Words: seasons

winter, spring, summer, fall

Let's draw pictures of each season: **winter, spring, summer,** and **fall.** Then you can tell me about your pictures, and we can label them with the right season name.

You Decide

Let's talk about what is happening in the first big picture. Then we can look at the small pictures. What will happen next? Let's talk about why you chose your picture. Then we can do the same thing with the pictures on the next page.

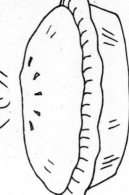

Conexión con el hogar

Queridos familiares:

Esta semana estamos leyendo *Our Special Sweet Potato Pie*. Un niño y su familia quieren hacer un pastel de camote para el cumpleaños del papá. Pero los camotes que recogen comienzan a rodar colina abajo. Toda la gente de la vecindad trata de agarrarlos. Estoy aprendiendo que puedo usar pistas del cuento, pistas de las ilustraciones y cosas que ya sé para deducir lo que el autor no dice. Por una de las ilustraciones me doy cuenta de que el Sr. Mason es dueño de la panadería.

MIS DESTREZAS DE LA SEMANA

Comprensión: hacer inferencias

Palabra de uso frecuente: have

Palabras de concepto: las estaciones

Fonética: C
Puedes usar pasas de uva u otros objetos pequeños para formar la letra **c**. Después podemos buscar palabras que empiecen con **c** en uno de tus libros.

Nombre _____

·······(Fold here)·······

© Macmillan/McGraw-Hill

Ejercicio de palabras

 Talk About it

VOCABULARIO

special   feast

¿Cuándo celebramos un día de fiesta? ¿Cuándo hacemos una fiesta de familia? ¿Qué tiene de especial esa fiesta?

MIS PALABRAS

Palabra de uso frecuente: have

¿Puedes escribir la palabra **have** en una tarjeta? Luego di oraciones que comiencen *I have _____*. Por ejemplo: *I have a coat.*

Palabras de concepto: las estaciones

cherry blossoms

Vamos a dibujar árboles de cerezo en flor y a pintar las flores de color rosa. Rotula el dibujo.

109

Lo decides tú

Vamos a platicar sobre lo que pasa en la primera ilustración grande. Luego podemos mirar las ilustraciones pequeñas de al lado. ¿Qué pasará después? Dime por qué escogiste esa ilustración. Hagamos lo mismo con las ilustraciones de la página siguiente.

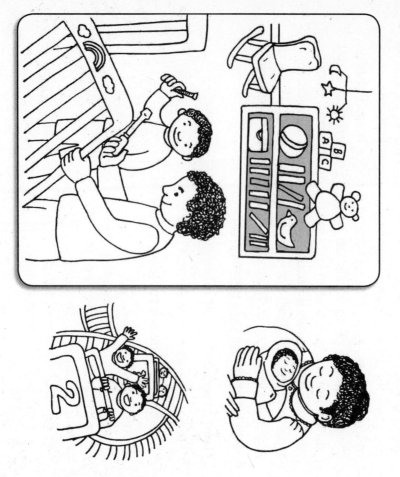

We Can!

by Lucy Floyd

4

Tim can sip milk .

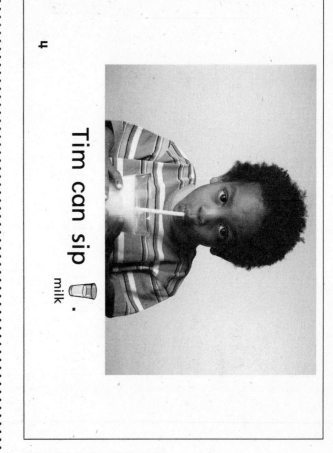

Have a cat nap, Tam!

8

Tip Cat can sip milk .

5

Nan can sit.

Nat Cat can sit.

We Can!

Can Tam Cat nap?

Sam can have a nap.

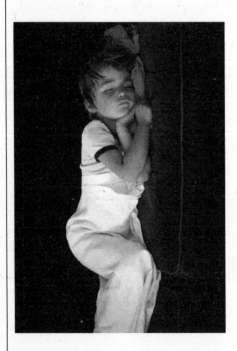

Let's Have Dinner

by Catherine Ellis

We can have muffins.

8

We can have milk.

2

Let's Have Dinner

© 2007 Macmillan/McGraw-Hill

We can have noodles.

7

We can have salad.

3

Let's Have Dinner

We can have hamburger.

6

4

We can have carrots.

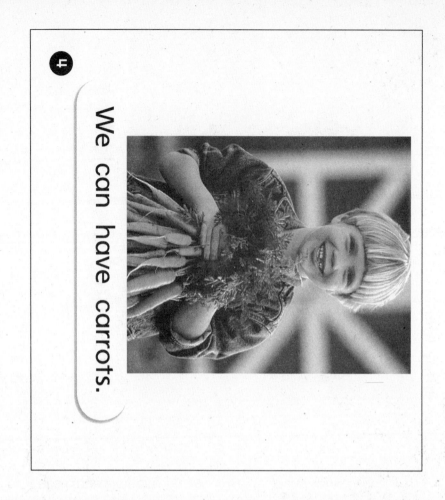

We can have corn.

5

Dear Family Member:

This week we are reading *Yoko*. Her mother makes her favorite lunch for school. But everyone laughs at it. Her teacher asks everyone to bring food from another country. I can use story clues to tell that steamed rice rolled up with something inside is called sushi.

This Week's Skills

Comprehension: make inferences

High-Frequency Word: to, have, go, see

Concept Words: season words

Phonics: n, c

I'll write a word and we can read it together. Then you can write the word. I am going to write: *no, not, nap, can, cat,* and *cap.*

Name _____

(fold here)

Word Workout

Talk About it

VOCABULARY

traditions   menus

Do we have any traditions in our family? What could we cook for a traditional family dinner?

MY WORDS TO KNOW

High-Frequency Words: to, have, go, see

I'll write each word on an index card and then say the word. You can point to each word I say. Can you read the word aloud?

Concept Words: foods, seasons

What kinds of food do we eat outside in the summer? What kinds of food do we eat in November and December?

Tic, Tac, Toe

We're going to play Tic, Tac, Toe. Choose one of the squares and tell me why the child is doing what the picture shows. Write an X in the square on the Tic, Tac, Toe board. We'll take turns; I'll write **Ms.** Whoever gets three in a row first wins!

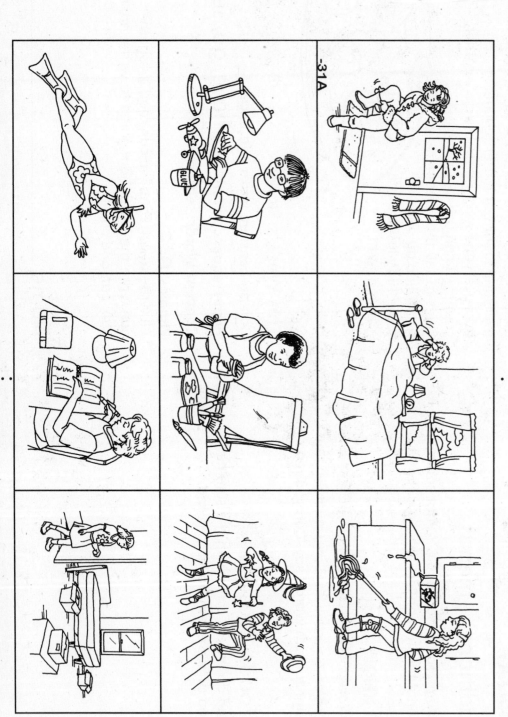

-31A-

Querido familiares:

Esta semana estamos leyendo *Yoko*. La mamá le prepara el almuerzo favorito de Yoko para que ella lo lleve a la escuela. Pero sus compañeros se ríen de lo que ella lleva. La maestra les pide a todos que traigan comidas de otros países. Puedo usar pistas del cuento para darme cuenta de que los rollos de arroz al vapor que tienen algo adentro se llaman sushi.

MIS DESTREZAS DE LA SEMANA

Comprensión: hacer inferencias

Palabras de uso frecuente: to, have, go, see

Palabras de concepto: las estaciones

Fonética: n, c
Voy a escribir una palabra y luego la podemos leer juntos. Después tú puedes escribirla: *no, not, nap, can, cat* y *cap.*

Nombre _____

(fold here)

Ejercicio de palabras

Talk About it

VOCABULARIO

traditions   menus

¿Tenemos tradiciones en nuestra familia? ¿Qué comida podríamos preparar para una cena familiar tradicional?

MIS PALABRAS

Palabras de uso frecuente: to, have, go, see

Voy a escribir cada palabra en una tarjeta y a decirla. Señala cada palabra que escuches. ¿Puedes leer la palabra en voz alta?

Palabras de concepto: foods, seasons

¿Qué tipo de comida (*foods*) comemos afuera en el verano? ¿Qué tipo de comida (*foods*) comemos en noviembre y diciembre?

Ta-te-ti

Vamos a jugar al Ta-Te-Ti. Escoge uno de los casilleros y explícame por qué el personaje está haciendo lo que se ve en el dibujo. Escribe una X en el casillero. Nos turnaremos. Yo voy a escribir letras **M**. Gana el que tenga tres marcas seguidas en una hilera.

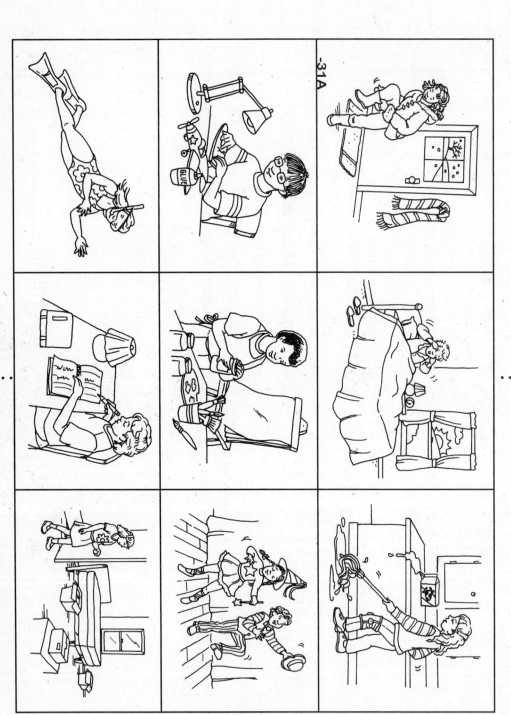

-31A

Nat

by Wiley Blevins

illustrated by Nathan Jarvis

Tip it in, Nat.

Nat

Tip it, Nat. Tip it!

Have a nap, Nat!

3

Tap an , Nat.
egg

See the pan, Nat?

© 2007 Macmillan/McGraw-Hill

Nat

Sit, Nat.

6

7

We can see it, Nat! Nat?

Thanksgiving

by Jane Frances

Thanksgiving

We have pie to eat.

We have soup to eat.

2

We have nuts to eat.

7

We have bread to eat.

3

We have turkey to eat.

6

4

We have corn to eat.

We have beans to eat.

5

Dear Family Member:

This week we are reading *Mama Cat Has Three Kittens*. Fluffy and Skinny do whatever Mama does. But not Boris! He's always getting into trouble. I'm learning how to use my own experiences and the pictures and details in a book to guess what will happen next. We are going to read about what Boris does when the other kittens nap.

This Week's Skills

Comprehension: make predictions

High-Frequency Word: is

Concept Words: positional terms

next to, on, off

Phonics: O

We can hunt for words that start with the letter **o** or have the letter **o** in them. I'm going to draw an octopus and write a word with **o** on each of the eight legs. You can underline each **o**.

Name _____

(fold here)

© Macmillan/McGraw-Hill

Word Workout

VOCABULARY

Talk About it

compare   actions

Think about two animals, such as a dog and a bird. How can we compare them? How are their actions alike and different?

MY WORDS TO KNOW

High-Frequency Word: is

What is your name? Tell me saying: *My name is _____*. Spell **is** aloud and then write it using a red crayon. Let's do it again using a blue crayon. Can you write **is** using a green crayon?

Concept Words:

next to, on, off

I'm going to put something **on** our table. Now you can take it **off** the table. Now put it **next to** the table. Let's choose something else to put on the table and play again.

What Will Happen?

For each picture on the left, draw a line to the picture on the right that shows what you think will happen next. Then we can do the same with the pictures on the next page. Let's talk about your choice.

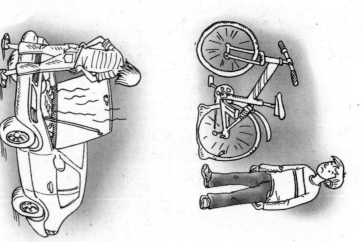

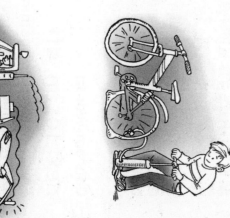

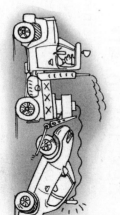

Conexión con el hogar

Queridos familiares:

Esta semana estamos leyendo *Mama Cat Has Three Kittens*. Fluffy y Skinny hacen lo mismo que hace la mamá. ¡Pero Boris, no! ¿Boris siempre está metido en problemas? Estoy aprendiendo a usar mi propia experiencia y las ilustraciones y detalles del libro para adivinar qué pasará después. Vamos a leer sobre lo que hace Boris mientras los otros gatitos duermen.

MIS DESTREZAS DE LA SEMANA

Comprensión: hacer predicciones

Palabra de uso frecuente: is

Palabras de concepto: palabras que indican posición

next to, on, off

Fonética: O

Vamos a buscar palabras que empiezan con la letra **o** o que tienen la letra **o**. Voy a dibujar un *octopus* (pulpo) y escribirle una palabra con **o** en cada una de las ocho patas. Puedes subrayar todas las **o** que encuentres.

Nombre _____

© Macmillan/McGraw-Hill

·····(fold here)·····

Ejercicio de palabras

Talk About it

VOCABULARIO

compare   actions

Piensa en dos animales, como un perro y un pájaro. ¿Cómo los puedes comparar? ¿En qué se parecen y diferencian sus acciones?

MIS PALABRAS

Palabra de uso frecuente: is

What is your name? Contéstame: *My name is _____.* Deletrea *is* en voz alta. Escribe *is* con un creyón rojo. Ahora con uno azul. ¿Puedes escribir *is* con uno verde?

Palabras de concepto:

next to, on, off

Realice lo siguiente y dígale al niño en inglés lo que está haciendo. Tome un libro y póngalo sobre la mesa: *I'm putting the book on the table.* Luego dígale que lo quite de la mesa: *take it off the table.* Ahora dígale: *put it next to the table.* Elija otro objeto y jueguen otra vez.

129

¿Qué pasará?

Traza una línea desde cada ilustración de la izquierda hasta la ilustración de la derecha que indica lo que tú crees que pasará después. Luego haremos lo mismo con las ilustraciones de la página siguiente.

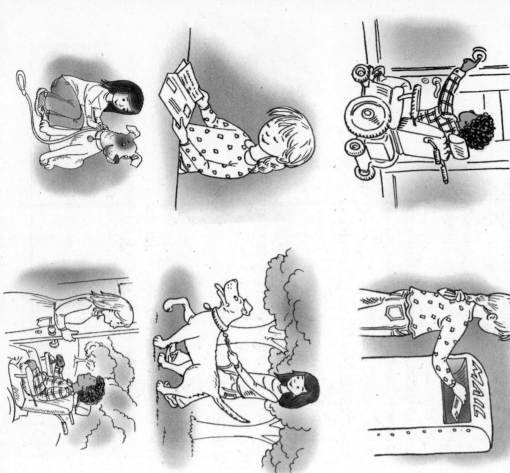

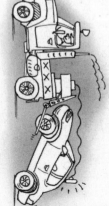

It is on a  log.

Sit On It

It can sit on ice.

Sit On It

by Tom Beedy

It can not sit!

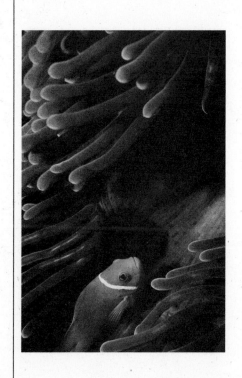

It can sit in Mom.

It can sit in a tree .

Sit On It

It can sit on a rock .

It is on top.

Animals in Nature

by K.C. Childs

It is on the log.

8

It is on the rock.

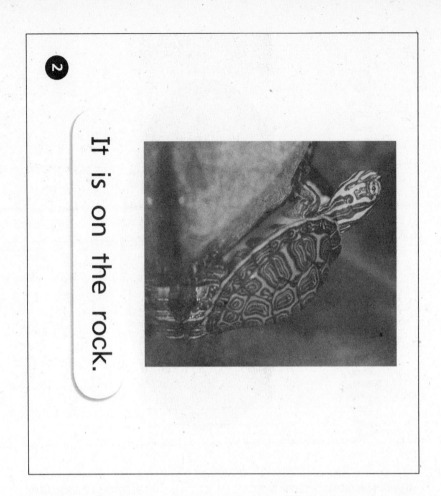

2

Animals in Nature

© 2007 Macmillan/McGraw-Hill

It is on the branch.

7

It is on the lily pad.

It is on the tree.

4

It is on the leaf.

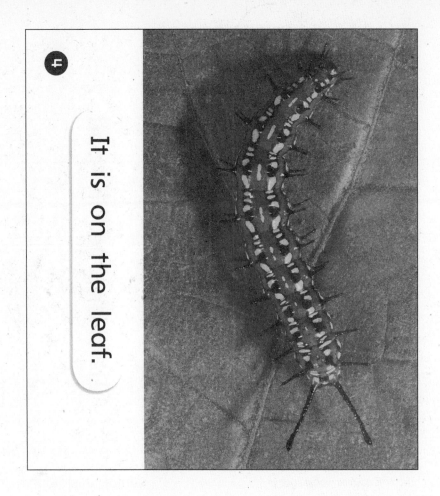

Animals in Nature © 2007 Macmillan/McGraw-Hill

It is on the flower.

5

Dear Family Member:

This week we are reading *Animal Babies ABC*. There is an animal baby for every letter of the alphabet! We are learning how to put things into groups. We figure out how things are alike and different so we can group them. For example, in this book, some animals hatch from eggs. Mothers give birth to others.

This Week's Skills

Comprehension: classify and categorize

High-Frequency Word: play

Concept Words: position words

Phonics: f

Have *family* members help your child *find* words that start with the letter **f** in book titles, on signs, and on other environmental print.

Name _____

·····(fold here)·····

© Macmillan/McGraw-Hill

Word Workout

Talk About It

VOCABULARY

parent   information

Talk about the different animal parents and babies your child has seen. Discuss what kind of information each animal baby learns from its parents.

MY WORDS TO KNOW

High-Frequency Word: play

Print the word *play* on an index card. Have your child use his or her arm to "write" it in the air, saying each letter while writing. You child can repeat this a few times until it can be done without looking at the card.

Concept Words: position words

around, down, left, right, up

Offer directions for your child to follow. You might suggest that your child wave his or her **left** hand; put the hand **down**; touch his or her **right** shoe; look **around** the room; look **up** at the ceiling.

Land or Water?

Invite your child to color the animals in red that live in places like those of the fox. Have your child color the animals in blue that live in places such as the fish.

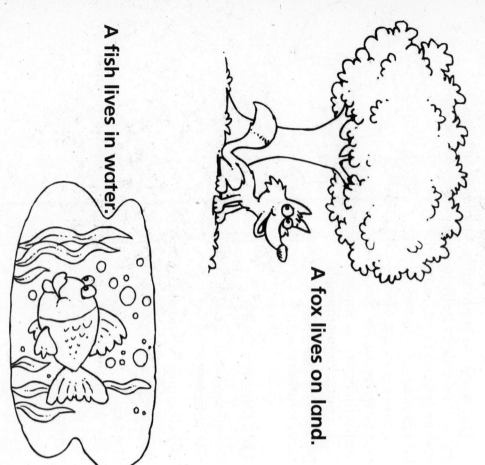

A fox lives on land.

A fish lives in water.

Queridos familiares:

Esta semana estamos leyendo *Animal Babies ABC*. Hay un bebé de animal para cada letra del alfabeto. Estamos aprendiendo a poner las cosas en grupos. Observamos en qué se parecen y en qué se diferencian para poder agruparlas. Por ejemplo, en este libro hay algunos animales que nacen de un huevo. Otros salen directamente de las mamás.

MIS DESTREZAS DE LA SEMANA

Comprensión: clasificar y categorizar

Palabra de uso frecuente: play

Palabras de concepto: palabras que indican posición

Fonética: f

Haga que otros miembros de la *familia* ayuden a su niño a buscar palabras que comiencen con la letra f en títulos de libros, carteles y otro material impreso a su alcance.

Nombre _____

(Fold here)

Ejercicio de palabras

Talk About it

VOCABULARIO

parent   information

Hable sobre animales jóvenes y adultos que su niño haya visto. Conversen sobre la información que cada bebé de animal aprende de sus padres.

MIS PALABRAS

Palabra de uso frecuente: play

Escriba *play* en una tarjeta en letras de imprenta. Haga que su niño la "escriba" en el aire y que diga cada letra a medida que escribe. El niño puede repetir esta actividad varias veces hasta que la pueda hacer sin mirar la tarjeta.

Palabras de concepto: palabras que indican posición

around, down, left, right, up

Déle instrucciones a su niño en inglés. Dígale que mueva su mano izquierda: *move your left hand;* que baje la mano: *put your hand down;* que se toque el pie derecho: *touch your right foot;* que mire alrededor o que mire hacia arriba: *look around the room, look up at the ceiling.*

¿Tierra o agua?

Pídale a su niño que coloree de rojo los animales que viven en lugares similares a donde vive el zorro. Dígale que coloree de azul los animales que viven en lugares similares a donde vive el pez.

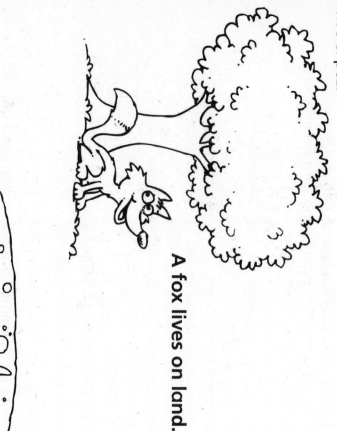

A fox lives on land.

A fish lives in water.

Can It Fit?

by Liz Ray

Can a  play?

hamster

It can play.

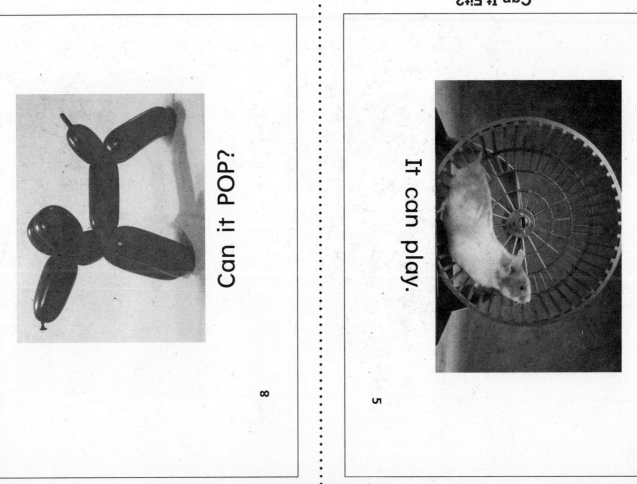

5

Can it POP?

8

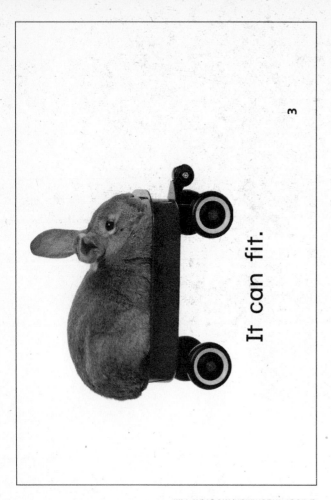

It can fit.

3

2

Can a rabbit fit?

Can It Fit?

Is it fat?

6

It is fat!

7

Animals and Their Babies

by Jan Dree

The squirrels can play.

8

The bears can play.

2

The fawns can play.

7

The foxes can play.

Animals and Their Babies

The goats can play.

4

The kittens can play.

Animals and Their Babies © 2007 Macmillan/McGraw-Hill

The foals can play.

5

Dear Family Member:

This week we are reading *Mole and the Baby Bird*. Mole helps a baby bird that falls out of its nest. He wants to keep it as a pet. His mother tells him the bird is a wild animal and wants to be free. I wonder what will happen to the bird. I'm learning about the characters in a story and about the plot. The plot is what happens.

This Week's Skills

Comprehension: identify character and plot

High-Frequency Words: is, play
I'll write **is**, **have**, **to**, **go**, and **play** on cards. When I say one of the words, point to it.

Concept Words: position words

Phonics: at, am, an, ap
Can you give me a rhyming word for **sat**? What about **ram**? **man**? and **map**?

Name _____

(fold here)

© Macmillan/McGraw-Hill

Word Workout

Talk About It

VOCABULARY

responsibility   habitat

A habitat is a place in nature where animals or people live. Talk about the responsibility we have to keep habitats safe for the animals that live there.

MY WORDS TO KNOW

High-Frequency Words: is, play

I am going to write these words on a piece of paper. We can read the words several times. Then we can talk about a playground. *What is there? What do you play?* We will try to use all the words as we talk.

Concept Words: position words

under, behind, down, left, next to, off, on, right, up

I'm going to put a spoon and a box on our table. I will tell you where to move it. For example: *Put the spoon next to the box; Put the spoon on the box.*

My Friend Amy

Suppose that Amy is your friend. Let's talk about what she is like. Then you can draw her. On the next page, let's talk about a day Amy went bicycle riding. I'll write sentences in the box.

Amy is my friend.

Amy got on her bike.

Amy came home.

Queridos familiares:

Esta semana estamos leyendo *Mole and the Baby Bird*. El topo le da ayuda a un pajarito que se ha caído del nido. Quiere tenerlo como mascota. Su mamá le dice que el pájaro no es un animal doméstico y que quiere estar en libe Me pregunto qué le va a pasar al pá Estoy aprendiendo sobre los personc y el argumento de un cuento. El argumento es lo que pasa.

MIS DESTREZAS DE LA SEMANA

Comprensión: identificar personajes y argumento

Palabras de uso frecuente: is, play

Voy a escribir *is, have, to, go y play* en tarjetas. Cuando yo diga una de las palabras, debes señalarla.

Palabras de concepto: palabras que indican posición

Fonética: at, am, an, ap

¿Me puedes decir una palabra que rime con *sat*? ¿Y con *ram*? ¿Con *man*? ¿Y con *map*?

Nombre _____

(Fold here)

© Macmillan/McGraw-Hill

Ejercicio de palabras

Talk About it

VOCABULARIO

responsibility   habitat

El hábitat es el lugar de la naturaleza donde vive un animal. Hablen sobre la responsabilidad que tenemos de mantener los hábitats seguros para los animales.

MIS PALABRAS

Palabras de uso frecuente: is, play

Voy a escribir estas palabras en una hoja de papel. Leámoslas varias veces. Después vamos a hablar de un parque de juegos. *What is there? What do you play?* Tratemos de usar todas las palabras de la lista.

Palabras de concepto: palabras que indican posición

under, behind, down, left, next to, off, on, right, up

Voy a poner una cuchara y una caja sobre la mesa. Te voy a pedir que muevas la cuchara y te voy a decir dónde ponerla. Por ejemplo: *Put the spoon next to the box. Put the spoon on the box.*

Mi amiga Amy

Imagina que Amy es tu amiga. Cuéntame cómo es. Después puedes dibujarla. En la próxima página vamos a hablar de un día en que Amy fue a montar en bicicleta. Voy a escribir oraciones en el recuadro.

Amy is my friend.

Amy got on her bike.

Amy came home.

Tap, Tap, Tap!

by Amy Helfer
illustrated by Nathan Jarvis

"A cat can not tap."

A  can tap!

bird

Tap, Tap, Tap!

Tap, tap, tap!

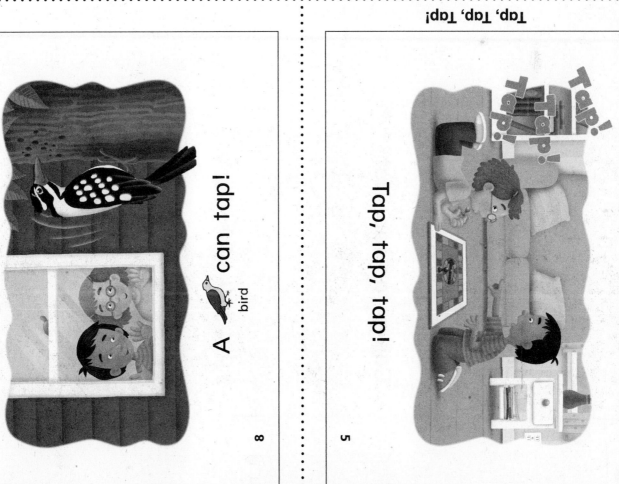

3

"Can a cat tap, Pam?"

2

Tap, tap, tap!

© 2007 Macmillan/McGraw-Hill

Tap, Tap, Tap!

"Can a fan tap, Nat?"

6

"A fan can not tap."

7

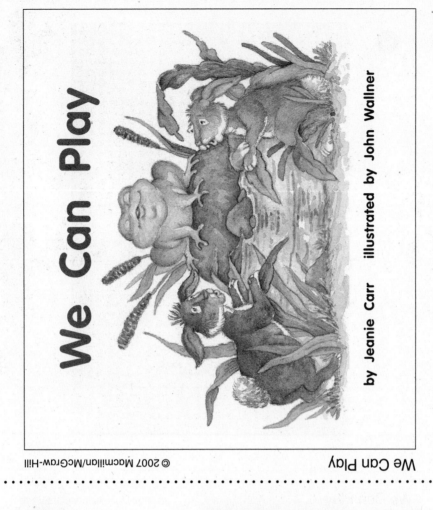

We Can Play

by Jeanie Carr   illustrated by John Wallner

We can play!

8

2

Can we play?

The bird is in the nest.

7

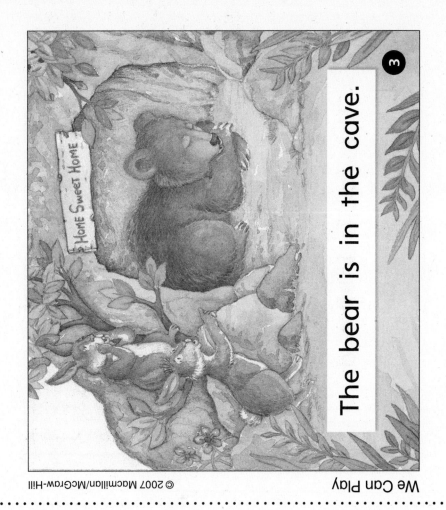

We Can Play

The bear is in the cave.

3

The frog is on the rock.

6

4

The fox is in the den.

The spider is on the web.

5

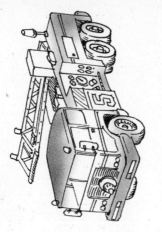

Dear Family Member:

This week we are reading *Russ and the Firehouse*. It's about a boy named Russ who visits his uncle in a firehouse. Russ gets to help his uncle. He helps clean the fire truck! I'm learning that every book has a main idea. It's what the book is mostly about. Details tell more about the main idea. This book is about a firehouse. The details tell us what is in a firehouse.

This Week's Skills

Comprehension: main idea and details

High-Frequency Word: are

Concept Words: sequence words

Phonics: h
Let's **hunt** for words in our **home** that begin with the letter h.

Name _____

(fold here)

© Macmillan/McGraw-Hill

Word Workout

 Talk About It

VOCABULARY

neighborhood   equipment

Try to take a walk around your neighborhood, or discuss stores and other places in the community. Have your child tell details about the type of equipment found at one or more places.

MY WORDS TO KNOW

High-Frequency Word: are

In large print, write the word **are** on a piece of paper. Read the word with your child. Have your child finger-trace the word as she or he says the letters. Then make up sentences together that begin *We are* _____.

Concept Words: sequence words

first, last, next

Line up three stuffed animals or toys. Ask your child: Which one is **first**? Which one is **next**? Which one is **last**? Reorder the animals and repeat. Find other objects to place in order.

What Am I?

We are going to answer riddles. When you know the answer to the riddle, tell me what to write in the box.

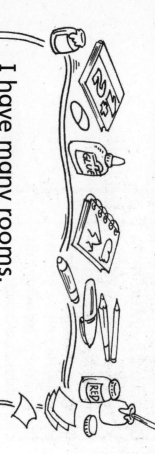

I have many rooms.
Teachers are in each room.

I have trees
and grass.
I have benches to
sit on.

I have tables
and chairs.
You can eat here.
A waiter gives
you food.

I sell all kinds
of bread.
I sell cakes and
cookies, too.

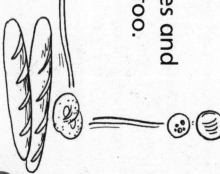

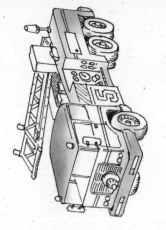

Conexión con el hogar

Queridos familiares:

Esta semana estamos leyendo *Russ and the Firehouse*. Trata de un niño llamado Russ que va a visitar a su tío en la estación de bomberos. Russ ayuda a su tío. ¡Lo ayuda a limpiar el camión de bomberos! Estoy aprendiendo que todos los libros tienen una idea principal, que es sobre lo que trata el libro. Los detalles nos dan más información sobre la idea principal. Este libro trata de una estación de bomberos. Los detalles nos explican qué hay en la estación.

MIS DESTREZAS DE LA SEMANA

Comprensión: idea principal y detalles

Palabra de uso frecuente: are

Palabras de concepto: palabras que indican orden

Fonética: h
Vamos a buscar palabras que comiencen con la letra h en nuestro hogar.

Nombre _____

(fold here)

© Macmillan/McGraw-Hill

Ejercicio de palabras

 Talk About It

VOCABULARIO

neighborhood   equipment

Dé una vuelta alrededor de su barrio o platique sobre tiendas y otros lugares de la comunidad con su niño. Haga que su niño le cuente detalles sobre los tipos de equipo que se pueden encontrar en uno o más de esos lugares.

MIS PALABRAS

Palabra de uso frecuente: are

Escriba la palabra are en letras de imprenta grandes en una hoja de papel. Lea la palabra con su niño. Haga que su niño trace la palabra con el dedo a medida que va diciendo las letras. Luego formen juntos oraciones que comiencen con *We are* _____ .

Palabras de concepto: palabras que indican orden

first, last, next

Ponga en fila tres animales de peluche o juguetes. Pregúntele a su niño: *Which one is first? Which one is next? Which one is last?* Cambie el orden y repita. Haga lo mismo con otros objetos.

159

¿Qué soy?

Vamos a averiguar las respuestas de estas adivinanzas. Cada vez que encuentres una respuesta, dímela y yo la escribo.

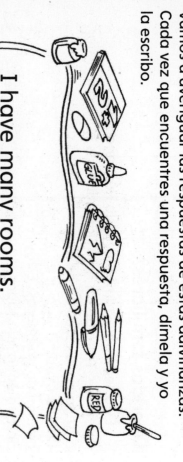

I have many rooms.
Teachers are in each room.

I have trees
and grass.
I have benches to
sit on.

I have tables
and chairs.
You can eat here.
A waiter gives
you food.

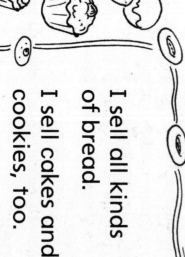

I sell all kinds
of bread.
I sell cakes and
cookies, too.

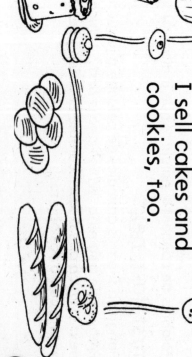

Hat, Cap, Hat

by Rosa Acosta

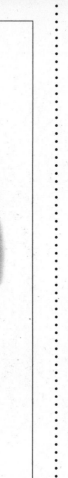

A hat is on Min.
Min can sip, sip.

We are on top.
Pat can hit it.

A hat is on Sam.
Sam can tip it!

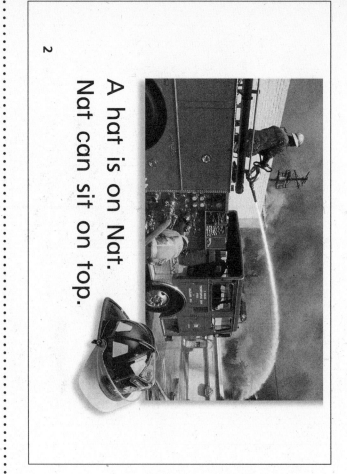

A hat is on Nat.
Nat can sit on top.

2

A cap is on Tom.
Tom can fit him in.

3

Hat, Cap, Hat

A cap is on Tim.
Tim can hit, hit, hit.

6

A hat is on Pam.
Pam can pat Tip.

7

Where Are We?

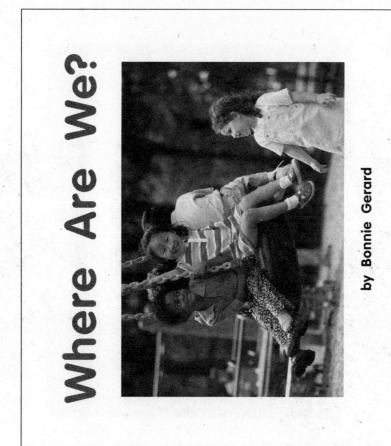

by Bonnie Gerard

We are at the zoo.

8

We are at the school.

2

We are at the hat store.

7

We are at the market.

3

We are at the park.

6

We are at the playground.

4

We are at the firehouse.

5

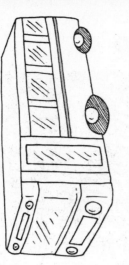

Dear Family Member:

This week we are reading *Bus Stops*. In this book, a bus stops at many places in a city. At each stop, I can look at the pictures that show things in the city. I'm learning that every book has a main idea. This book is about all the things you can see from a bus window.

This Week's Skills

Comprehension: main idea and details

High-Frequency Words: for, you

Concept Words: words that compare

Phonics: d, r

Let's think of words that begin with the letters **d** and **r**. They stand for the sound you hear at the beginning of the words *dog* and *rock*. I'll give you clues to guess the word that begins with **d** or **r**. For example: *I use a shovel to do this* or *I use my umbrella when it is doing this outside.*

Name _____

(fold here)

Word Workout

Talk About it

VOCABULARY

community   workers

Let's talk about some different workers we see when we go outdoors. For example, a mail carrier brings us our mail. *(construction workers, bus drivers, police officers)*

MY WORDS TO KNOW

High-Frequency Words: for, you

Look for the words *for* and *you* in cards, in books, in advertisements, and anywhere else that has printed words. I'm going to give you a piece of paper and you can draw a picture. Then I'll fold the paper in half to make a card. Write the name of someone you will give the card to.

Concept Words: words that compare

big, bigger, biggest

We can play "I Spy." I'll say things such as, *I spy two dogs. Which one is bigger? Which one is the biggest?* Then you can ask me a **big/bigger/biggest** question.

What's Going On?

Look at the picture. What is the main idea? What details tell about the main idea? Color all the details that belong in the town. Cross out the details that do not belong.

Conexión con el hogar

Queridos familiares:

Esta semana estamos leyendo *Bus Stops*. Es sobre un autobús que para en distintos lugares. En cada parada veo ilustraciones de algo de la ciudad. Estoy aprendiendo que todos los libros tienen una idea principal. Este libro trata de todas las cosas que se ven desde la ventanilla de un autobús.

MIS DESTREZAS DE LA SEMANA

Comprensión: idea principal y detalles

Palabras de uso frecuente: for, you

Palabras de concepto: palabras que comparan

Fonética: d, r

Vamos a pensar en palabras que comiencen con **d** y **r**. Representan el sonido al comienzo de las palabras *dog* y *rock*. Te voy a dar pistas para que adivines cuál es la palabra que comienza con **d** o con **r**, por ejemplo: *I use a shovel to do this*, o *I use my umbrella when it is doing this outside.*

Nombre _____

© Macmillan/McGraw-Hill

·· (fold here) ··

Ejercicio de palabras

Talk About It

VOCABULARIO

community   workers

Hablemos sobre trabajadores que vemos cuando salimos. Por ejemplo, un cartero (*mail carrier*) nos trae las cartas. (*construction workers, bus drivers, police officers*)

MIS PALABRAS

Palabras de uso frecuente: for, you

Busca las palabras **for** y **you** en tarjetas, libros, anuncios y cualquier otro lugar donde haya palabras impresas. Te voy a dar una hoja de papel para que hagas un dibujo. Doblaré el papel en dos para hacer una tarjeta. Escribe el nombre de la persona a quien se la darás.

Palabras de concepto: palabras que comparan

big, bigger, biggest

Vamos a jugar a "I Spy" (Veo, veo). Te voy a decir, por ejemplo: *I spy two dogs. Which one is bigger? Which one is the biggest?* Después tú me puedes hacer una pregunta con **big/bigger/biggest.**

169

¿Qué pasa aquí?

Mira la ilustración. ¿Cuál es la idea principal? ¿Qué detalles se refieren a la idea principal? Colorea todos los detalles que correspondan a la ciudad. Tacha los detalles que no correspondan.

Rod Can See It

by Nancy Hertz

4

Rod can see Tad mop.
Tad can dip the mop.

The mat is for Pat.
Pat can nap on it.

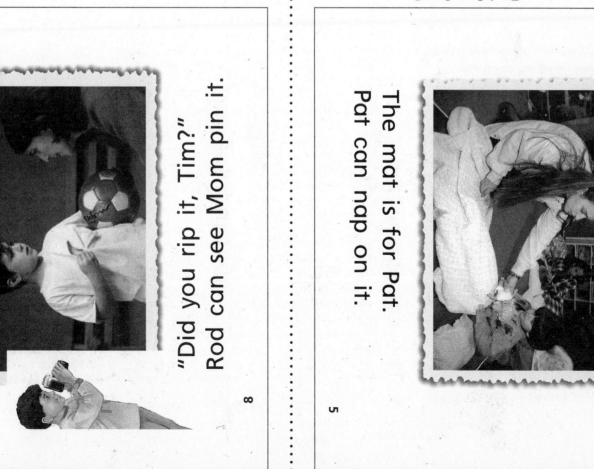

5

"Did you rip it, Tim?"
Rod can see Mom pin it.

8

Rod can see Don play it.
Did Don hit the rim?

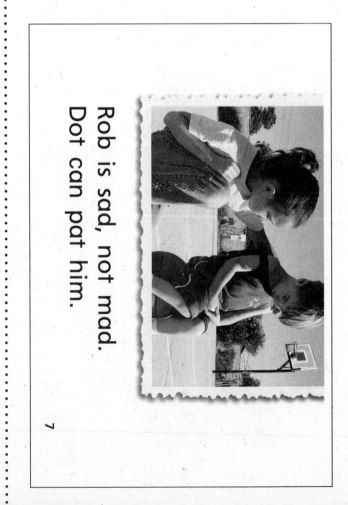

Rob is sad, not mad.
Dot can pat him.

Mom ran to Ron.
Ron did not tip it.

Rod Can See It

The cat sat on top.
Rod can see it sit.

This Is for You

by Lee Peters   illustrated by Noah Jones

The card is for you!

8

The rose is for you.

This Is for You © 2007 Macmillan/McGraw-Hill

The basket is for you.

7

The picture is for you.

3

The doll is for you.

6

The ball is for you.

This Is for You

The kitten is for you.

5

Home-School Connection

Dear Family Member:

This week we are reading *Alicia's Happy Day*. In this book a girl walks in her neighborhood with her mother. They hear music on the street. They see flags and taxicabs. Everything Alicia sees makes her feel happy. I'm learning to check if I understand a story by retelling it in my own words. The pictures in the book help me recall what I read.

This Week's Skills

Comprehension: retell

High-Frequency Words: for, you, are

Concept Words: sequence words

Phonics: ad, at, an, ap, am
Look at these letters. They end many words. Let's find or say words that end with those letters. For example, we could say: sad or bad.

Name _____

(Fold here)

Word Workout

Talk About it

VOCABULARY

celebration   jobs

Let's talk about a celebration you enjoy. What jobs need to be done, in order, to plan the celebration?

MY WORDS TO KNOW

High-Frequency Words: for, you, are

I'll write each word on a sticky note. We can read and say the words. In the next book we read, you can stick each note on the page where you find the word.

Concept Words: sequence words

first, next, last

Let's talk about a making a sandwich. Tell me what needs to be done **first, next,** and **last** in order to make the sandwich.

Tell It All!

Have your child retell the story of "The Three Little Pigs." (First read or tell the story if your child is unfamiliar with it.) Point to each picture as your child describes what is happening. Then your child can color his or her favorite picture.

Queridos familiares:

Esta semana estamos leyendo *Alicia's Happy Days*. En este libro una niña camina por su vecindario con su madre. Las dos escuchan música en la calle. Ven banderas y taxis. Todo lo que Alicia ve la hace sentirse feliz. Estoy aprendiendo a ver si comprendo un cuento al contarlo con mis propias palabras. Las ilustraciones de un libro me ayudan a recordar lo que leo.

MIS DESTREZAS DE LA SEMANA

Comprensión: volver a contar

Palabras de uso frecuente: for, you, are

Palabras de concepto: palabras que indican sucesión

Fonética: ad, at, an, ap, am

Mira estas letras. Vamos a buscar o a decir palabras que terminen con ellas. Por ejemplo, *sad* o *bad*.

Nombre _____

Ejercicio de palabras

Talk About it

VOCABULARIO

celebration   jobs

Vamos a platicar sobre una celebración que te guste. ¿Qué tareas hay que hacer para organizar la celebración?

MIS PALABRAS

Palabras de uso frecuente: for, you, are

Voy a escribir cada una de estas palabras en una nota adhesiva. Vamos a leer las palabras juntos y a decirlas. En el próximo libro que leamos, podrás pegar la nota adhesiva en la página donde encuentres la palabra.

Palabras de concepto: palabras que indican sucesión

first, next, last

Vamos a hablar sobre cómo preparar un sándwich. Dime qué necesitamos hacer *first, next, last* (primero, luego y por último) para preparar el sándwich.

¡Cuéntamelo!

Haga que su niño le vuelva a contar el cuento "Los tres cerditos". Primero léale el cuento o cuénteselo si el niño no lo conoce. Señale cada ilustración a medida que el niño vaya narrando lo que pasa. Después el niño puede colorear su ilustración favorita.

Dad Can Pin It On

by Amy Helfer
illustrated by Nathan Jarvis

"It is a fat cat, Dad.
Mom can pat him!"

"Mom can not pat him."

5

"Pin it on, Dad."
Dad can pin it on Mom!

8

"Not a cap, Sam."

"It is a tan cap, Dad.
Can it fit on Mom?"

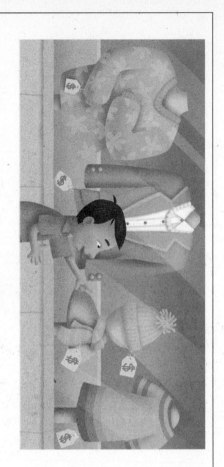

Dad Can Pin It On

"Is it a red pin on top?
Is it a red pin, Dad?"

"It is a pin, Sam!
It is a red pin!"

Panda House

by Marie Stone   illustrated by John Wallner

We did it for you!

8

We are digging for you.

2

We are happy for you.

7

We are building for you.

Panda House

3

We are planting for you.

6

4

We are painting for you.

We are washing for you.

5

Home-School Connection

Dear Family Member:

This week we are reading *A Rainy Day*. The book has photographs. The words and pictures tell what a rainy day is like. It is wet and gray. A lot of rain can make floods. The main idea of this book is about rain. The writer gives a lot of details about what happens when it rains.

This Week's Skills

Comprehension: identify main idea and details

High-Frequency Words: this, do

Concept Words: sound words

Phonics: e

When we go out, let's look for words that start with the letter e. We can look in stores or other places we visit. We might find words such as *enter* and *exit*.

Name _____

· (fold here) ·

© Macmillan/McGraw-Hill

Word Workout

VOCABULARY

Talk About It

weather   cloud

What can we say about today's weather? Is there rain? Look at the sky for clouds. Talk about how clouds can sometimes help us predict the weather.

MY WORDS TO KNOW

High-Frequency Words: this, do

I'm going to write the words **this** and **do** on a piece of paper. We can read them together. You can finger-trace each word as you say the letters. Let's look around our kitchen. Point to different things and take turns asking: *What can this thing do? Our refrigerator keeps food cold.*

Concept Words: sound words

bam, crack, drip, drop, splash

Let's play "I Hear" using words for sounds. For example: *I hear something drip in the sink. What is it? I hear something go bam after lightning. What is it? I hear someone splash in the bathtub. Who is it?*

187

What Am I?

Let's read the riddles below. You can draw a line to match the riddles to the answers.

You see me
in the sky.
Then you hear
a loud bam!

I look like popcorn
in the sky.
Sometimes I look
like animals.

I warm up the earth.
I look round and
yellow.

When it snows
you are cold.
I keep your
hands warm.

I keep your feet dry.
You can splash
in puddles.

I can play in
the water.
You wear me
in a pool.

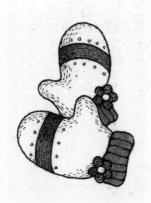

Conexión con el hogar

Queridos familiares:

Esta semana estamos leyendo *A Rainy Day*. En el libro hay fotografías. Las palabras y las ilustraciones nos dicen cómo es un día de lluvia. Es húmedo y gris. Cuando llueve mucho puede haber inundaciones. La idea principal de este libro es la lluvia. El escritor da muchos detalles de lo que pasa cuando llueve.

MIS DESTREZAS DE LA SEMANA

Comprensión: identificar la idea principal y los detalles.

Palabras de uso frecuente: this, do

Palabras de concepto: palabras de sonido

Fonética: e
Cuando salgamos vamos a buscar palabras que comiencen con la letra e. Vamos a mirar en las tiendas y en otros lugares. Tal vez encontremos palabras como *enter* y *exit.*

Nombre _____

······· (fold here) ·······

© Macmillan/McGraw-Hill

Ejercicio de palabras

Talk About it

VOCABULARIO

weather   cloud

¿Qué podemos decir del tiempo de hoy? ¿Llueve? Busquen nubes en el cielo. Hablen de cómo las nubes pueden a veces ayudarnos a predecir el tiempo.

MIS PALABRAS

Palabras de uso frecuente: this, do

Voy a escribir las palabras *this* y *do.* Luego las leeremos juntos. Traza cada palabra con el dedo mientras dices las letras. Vamos a la cocina. Voy a señalar cosas y a preguntarte: *What can this thing do?* Tú debes responderme, por ejemplo: *Our refrigerator keeps food cold.*

Palabras de concepto: palabras de sonido

bam, crack, drip, drop, splash

Vamos a jugar a "Escucho algo..." con palabras en inglés que representan sonidos. Presta atención: *Escucho algo que hace* **drip** *en el fregadero. ¿Qué es? Oigo algo que hace* **bam** *después de un relámpago. ¿Qué es? Alguien hace* **splash** *en la tina del baño. ¿Quién es?*

(189)

¿Qué soy?

Vamos a leer las adivinanzas de abajo. Tú puedes trazar una línea que vaya de la adivinanza a la respuesta.

You see me
in the sky.
Then you hear
a loud bam!

I look like popcorn
in the sky.
Sometimes I look
like animals.

I warm up the earth.
I look round and
yellow.

When it snows
you are cold.
I keep your
hands warm.

I keep your feet dry.
You can splash
in puddles.

I can play in
the water.
You wear me
in a pool.

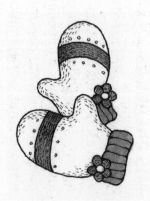

190

Ed Can, Ted Can

by Liz Ray

It is hot, hot, hot!
Dan can dip in.

Pit, pat. Pit, pat.
Pam can play in it.

8

Nan can hit at a net.
Nan can do it!

5

Ed is set to go.
Ed can do it!

The cat ran to Ted.
Ted can pet the cat.

Ed Can, Ted Can

Cam did this.
Fit a red hat on him!

6

Pit, pat. Pit, pat.
Kit can sit in the den.

7

What Can You Do?

by Frank Fenn

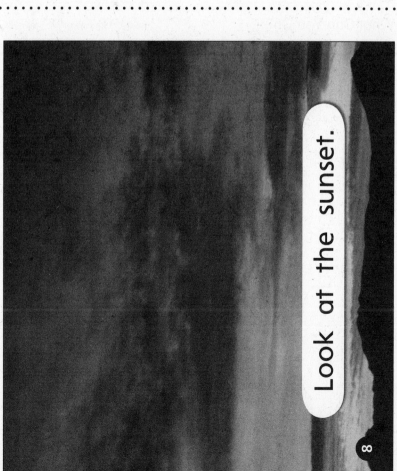

Look at the sunset.

8

Look at the rain.

What Can You Do?

You can do this.

You can do this.

3

Look at the snow.

6

4

Look at the clouds.

You can do this.

5

Home-School Connection

Dear Family Member:

We are reading *In the Yard* this week. At the beginning of the book, a girl and her parents plant flowers in their yard. The whole book is about things her family does in their yard. I'm learning that stories can happen in different places and at different times. This story tells us about a yard in all the seasons.

This Week's Skills

Comprehension: identify setting

High-Frequency Words: and, what

Concept Words: words that compare

Phonics: b, l

Let's hunt in books for words that begin with the letters **b** and **l**. We can point to the letter in each word we find and name it:

Name _____

ABK_HSC_U7W2_17A_193918

·········· (fold here) ··········

© Macmillan/McGraw-Hill

Word Workout

 Talk About It

VOCABULARY

season   month

Do we have a calendar? What month is it now? What season? We can look at other months and talk about what season they are in.

MY WORDS TO KNOW

High-Frequency Words: and, what

Let's look for the words **and** and **what** in book titles, on signs outdoors, and in newspapers. When we see a word, you can write the word in the air as you name the letters. Then we can write each word on a piece of paper.

Concept Words: words that compare

long, longer, longest

Let's arrange things by size. I'll put a long pen here, then a longer marker, and last the longest pencil. Now you tell me which is the longest.

When Is It?

Here's a game called "When Is It?" We need two small things for markers, such as a raisin and a piece of macaroni. Now we each flip a coin. We can move one place for "heads" and two places for "tails." When you land on a place, look at the picture. What season do you think the setting shows? We'll take turns. Whoever gets to the pool first wins!

Queridos familiares:

Esta semana estamos leyendo *In The Yard*. Al principio del libro, una niña planta flores en el jardín con sus padres. Todo el libro trata de cosas que la familia hace en el jardín. Estoy aprendiendo que los cuentos ocurren en diferentes lugares y en épocas distintas. Este cuento se refiere a un jardín en todas las estaciones.

MIS DESTREZAS DE LA SEMANA

Comprensión: identificar el ambiente

Palabras de uso frecuente: and, what

Palabras de concepto: palabras que comparan

Fonética: b, i

Vamos a buscar en libros palabras que comiencen con **b** y con **i**. Vamos a señalar la letra en cada palabra que encontremos y a decir su nombre.

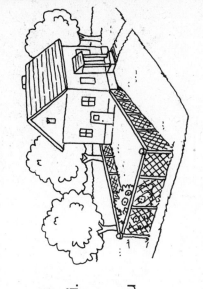

ABK_HSC_U7W2_17A_193918

Nombre _____

.... (fold here) ....

© Macmillan/McGraw-Hill

Ejercicio de palabras

Talk About it

VOCABULARIO

season   month

¿Hay aquí un calendario? ¿Qué mes es? ¿Qué estación? Podemos mirar otros meses y hablar de la estación que es.

MIS PALABRAS

Palabras de uso frecuente: and, what

Vamos a buscar las palabras *and* y *what* en títulos de libros, en carteles de la calle y en periódicos. Cuando veas una de las palabras, puedes escribirla en el aire y nombrar las letras. Luego podemos escribir las palabras en una hoja de papel.

Palabras de concepto: palabras que comparan

long, longer, longest

Vamos a ordinar cosas de tamaño. Voy a poner un bolígrafo que es **long** aquí, luego un marcador que es **longer** al lado y finalmente el lápiz que es **longest**. Dime ¿Cuál es **longest**?

¿Cuándo es?

Aquí hay un juego que se llama "¿Qué es?" Necesitamos dos fichas pequeñas como una pasa de uva y un trozo de macarrón. Vamos a echar una moneda. Avanzaremos un espacio si sacamos *heads*, y dos si sacamos *tails*. Cuando llegues a un lugar mira la ilustración, ¿qué estación del año muestra? Gana el primero que llegue a la piscina.

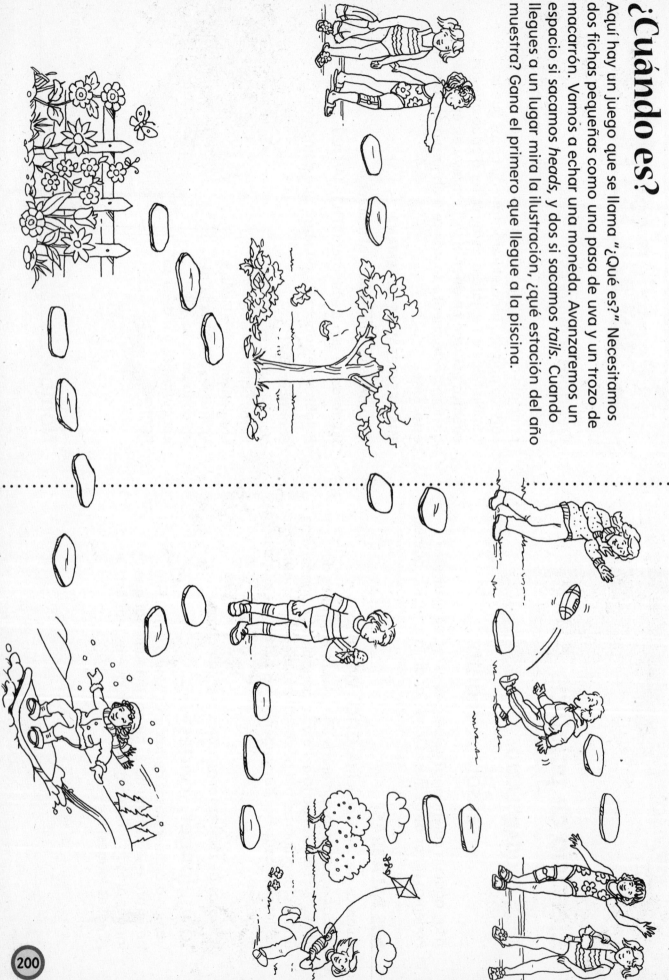

Hot Ben, Hot Lin

by Liz Ray

It is hot, hot, hot!
Dan can dip in.

4

Nan can hit at a net.
Nan can do it!

5

Pit, pat. Pit, pat.
Pam can play in it.

8

Hot Ben, Hot Lin

Dad let Lin swim a lap.
Dad let Ben hop in.

3

Lin and Ben are hot, hot, hot.
They do not have a cap.

2

It is not hot.
What can fit on Deb?

6

They can fit on Deb.
Deb, Kit, and Pam can go.

7

Go and Play

by Katherine Scraper
illustrated by Elise Mills

See what bears do?
Go to bed, Cub!

8

See what birds do?
You can too!

2

© 2007 Macmillan/McGraw-Hill

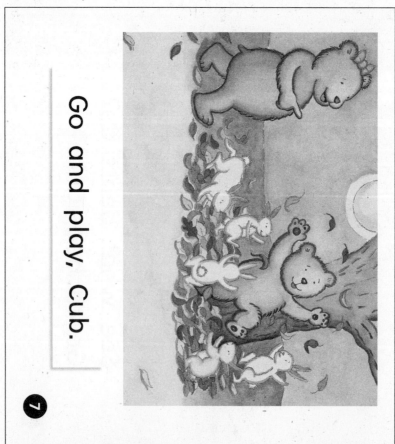

Go and play, Cub.

7

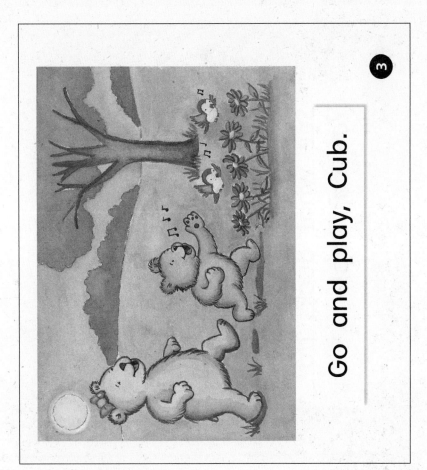

Go and play, Cub.

Go and Play

3

See what rabbits do?
You can too!

6

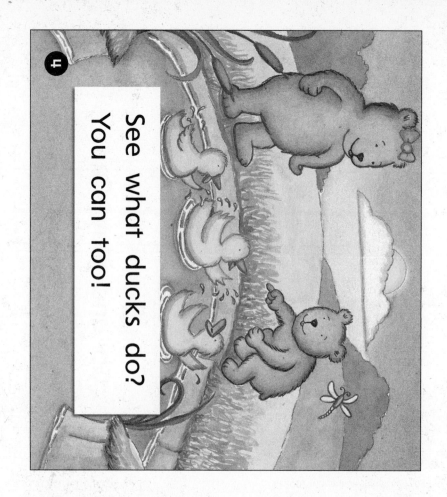

See what ducks do?
You can too!

4

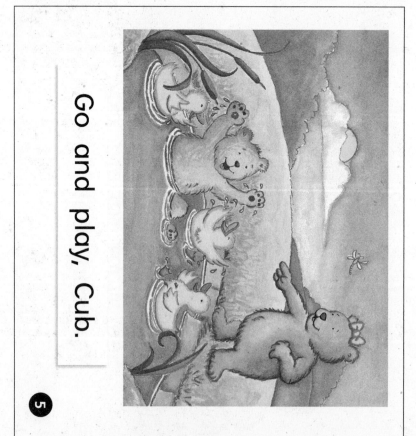

Go and play, Cub.

5

Dear Family Member:

This week we are reading *Bear Snores On*. It's about a bear that sleeps in a cave during winter. When a mouse comes into the cave, the bear keeps sleeping. A hare joins the mouse and they have snacks. But the bear keeps sleeping. This story tells about make-believe things that cannot happen in real life.

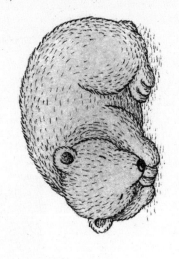

This Week's Skills

Comprehension: fantasy and reality

High-Frequency Words:
this, do, and, what

Concept Words: sound words

Phonics: it, ip, id
Can you think of a word that rhymes with **pit?**
What about **lip?**
What about **lid?**

Name _____

······ (fold here) ······

© Macmillan/McGraw-Hill

Word Workout

Talk About it

VOCABULARY

experience   hibernate

Discuss why birds fly south in the fall. Why do animals hibernate during the cold winter months? What do animals experience in the cold?

MY WORDS TO KNOW

High-Frequency Words:
this, do, and, what

Print the words in a list, then say a word and ask your child to point to it. Ask your child to copy the words.

Concept Words: sound words
bam, crack, drip, drop, splash

Ask: *What do you hear when you jump in a pool?* **splash**
What do you hear when rain falls? **drip, drop** *What do you hear when a bat hits a ball?* **crack** *What sound do you hear when you bang a drum?* **bam**

Get Real

Play the "Real or Fantasy" game with your child. Use two small objects for markers. First, flip a coin. Move one space for "heads" or two spaces for "tails." Then look at the picture in the box landed on. Does the picture show a fantasy, something that could not happen, or does it show reality, a thing that could happen in real life? Take turns. Whoever gets to the cave first wins!

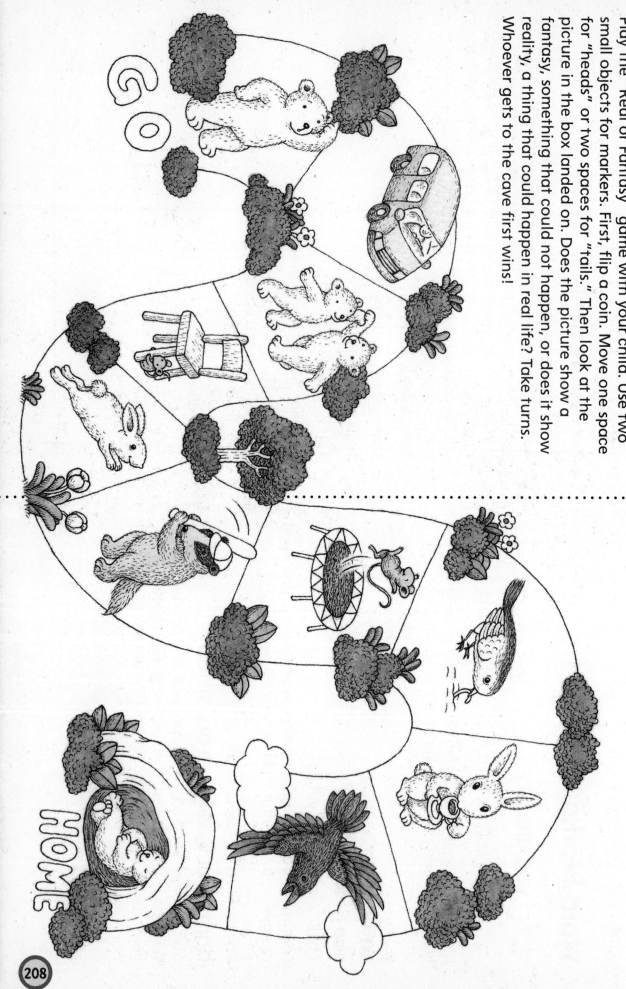

Conexión con el hogar

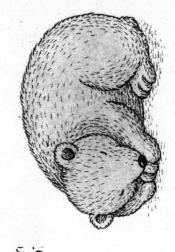

Queridos familiares:

Esta semana estamos leyendo *Bear Snores On.* Trata de un oso que duerme en una cueva durante el invierno. Cuando un ratón entra en la cueva, el oso continúa durmiendo. Una liebre se une al ratón y los dos comen algo. Pero el oso continúa durmiendo. El cuento es sobre cosas imaginarias, que no pueden pasar en la vida real.

MIS DESTREZAS DE LA SEMANA

Comprensión: fantasía y realidad

Palabras de uso frecuente:
this, do, and, what

Palabras de concepto: palabras de sonido

Fonética: it, ip, id
¿Se te ocurre alguna palabr que rime con *pit*? ¿Y con *lip*: ¿Y con *lid*?

Nombre _____

(fold here)

© Macmillan/McGraw-Hill

Ejercicio de palabras

 Talk About it

VOCABULARIO

experience   hibernate

Comente por qué los pájaros vuelan hacia el sur en otoño. ¿Por qué invernan los animales durante el invierno? ¿Qué experimentan los animales cuando hace frío?

MIS PALABRAS

Palabras de uso frecuente:
this, do, and, what

Haga una lista con las palabras y diga una palabra al azar y haga que su niño señale la palabra. Haga que el niño copie las palabras.

Palabras de concepto: palabras de sonido
bam, crack, drip, drop, splash

Pregúntele a su niño: ¿Qué sonido escuchas cuando chocan dos carros? *bam* ¿Qué sonido escuchas cuando te zambulles en la piscina? *splash* ¿Y escuchas cuando llueve? *drip, drop* ¿Y cuando el bate golpea la pelota? *crack* ¿Qué sonido escuchas cuando tocas el tambar? *bam*

209

¿Realidad o fantasía?

Juegue este juego de realidad o fantasía con su niño. Use como marcadores dos objetos pequeños. Primero, echen una moneda. Avancen un espacio si sale *heads* y dos si sale *tails*. Observen la ilustración del recuadro donde cayó la moneda. ¿Muestra la ilustración una fantasía o una realidad? Túrnense. Gana el que llegue primero a la cueva.

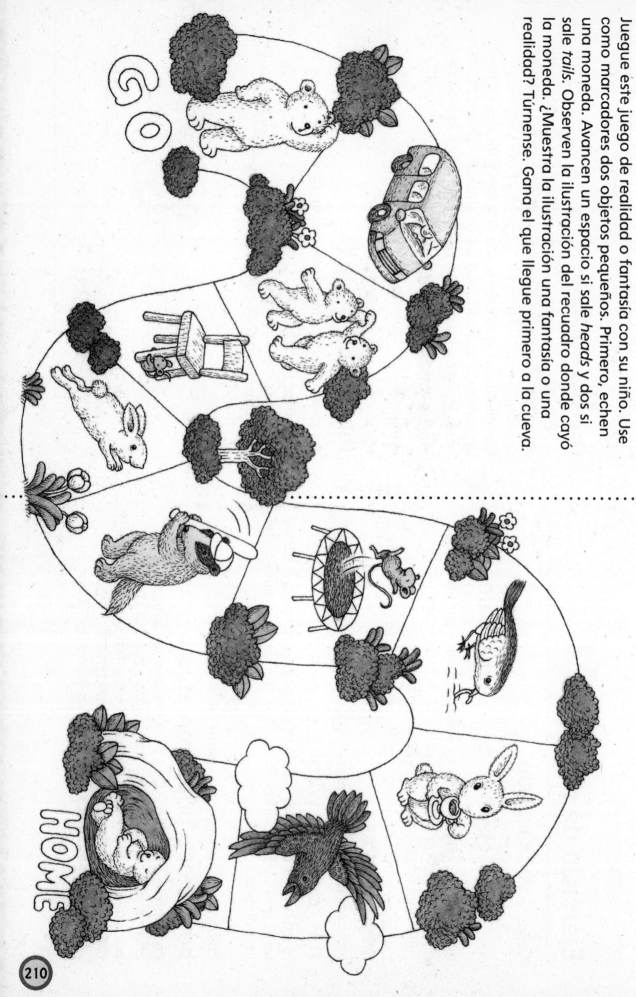

Pat and Tip

by Amy Helfer
illustrated by Nathan Jarvis

Sam can bat.
"Hit it, Sam! Hit it!"

Pat and Tip are not sad.
Pat can sit. Tip can nap!

8

Can Nat bat?
"Pop it, Nat! Pop it!"

5

"I have a bat.
Can you play?"

Nat can. Sam can.
Cam and Pam can.

Pat and Tip

Pit, pat. It is rain!
Pit, pit, pat. Let it rain!

Nat ran. Cam ran. Sam ran.
Pam, Pat, and Tip ran!

In the Snow

by Michael Price   illustrated by Steve Haskamp

See what bears do?
Go to bed, Cub!

8

This is Ben and Lin.

2

What can Ned do?
What can Deb do?

7

What can Ben do?
What can Lin do?

In the Snow

3

This is Ned and Deb.

6

This is Ted and Lil.

4

What can Ted do?
What can Lil do?

5

Dear Family Member:

This week we are reading *Oak Trees*. It tells about how oak trees grow from acorns. I'm learning that an oak tree grows in different steps. It starts as an acorn. Then it grows roots. Next a stem grows. Words like **first, next, later,** and **last** tell the order in which things happen.

This Week's Skills

Comprehension: identify sequence

High-Frequency Words: little, said

Concept Words: position words

Phonics: k, ck
How many words can we think of that begin with the letter **k** or end with the letters **ck**. We could say **k**id and ba**ck**.

ABK_HSC_U8W1_01A_193918

© Macmillan/McGraw-Hill

(Fold here)

Word Workout

 Talk About it

VOCABULARY

grow   plant

What kind of flowers would you like to plant? What would happen as they grow?

MY WORDS TO KNOW

High-Frequency Words: little, said

Let's find the words **said** and **little** in books. You can copy and complete this sentence: *I said, "A _____ is little."*

Concept Words: position words

bottom, top, middle

I'm drawing a picture of a ladder. Point to the top of the ladder. Point to the middle. Draw something at the bottom.

Name _____

Grandpa's Garden

Look at the pictures to see what Grandpa does in his garden. We can write a number next to each sentence to tell what order Grandpa does things in his garden.

Grandpa waits for the flowers to grow.

Grandpa digs holes.

Grandpa plants seeds.

Look at what Grandpa does now. We can write a number next to each sentence to tell what order Grandpa does things in his garden.

The flowers are growing.

Grandpa puts the flowers in a vase.

Grandpa cuts the flowers.

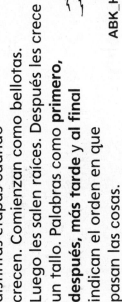

Queridos familiares:

Esta semana estamos leyendo *Oak Trees*. Cuenta cómo los árboles de roble crecen a partir de bellotas. Estoy aprendiendo que los árboles de roble pasan por distintas etapas cuando crecen. Comienzan como bellotas. Luego les salen raíces. Después les crece un tallo. Palabras como **primero, después, más tarde** y **al final** indican el orden en que pasan las cosas.

MIS DESTREZAS DE LA SEMANA

Comprensión: orden de los sucesos

Palabras de uso frecuente: little, said

Palabras de concepto: palabras que indican posición

Fonética: k, ck

¿Cuántas palabras sabemos en inglés que comienzan con la letra **k**? ¿Y qué terminan con **ck**? Para empezar tenemos dos: *kid* y *back*.

Nombre _____

ABK_HSC_U8W1_01A_193918

© Macmillan/McGraw-Hill

(fold here)

Ejercicio de palabras

VOCABULARIO

grow   plant

Talk About it

¿Qué clase de flores te gustaría plantar? ¿Qué les va a pasar a medida que crezcan?

MIS PALABRAS

Palabras de uso frecuente: little, said

Vamos a buscar las palabras *said* y *little* en libros. Puedes copiar esta oración y terminarla:

I said: "A _____ is little."

Palabras de concepto: palabras que indican posición

bottom, top, middle

Voy a dibujar una escalera. Indica con el dedo lo alto de la escalera. Indica con el dedo la media. Dibuja algo al pie.

El jardín del abuelo

Mira lo que está haciendo el abuelo en su jardín. Vamos a escribir un número al lado de cada oración para indicar en qué orden hace el abuelo las cosas del jardín.

Grandpa waits for the flowers to grow.

Grandpa digs holes.

Grandpa plants seeds.

Mira lo que el abuelo hace ahora. Hagamos lo mismo que hicimos en la página anterior.

The flowers are growing.

Grandpa puts the flowers in a vase.

Grandpa cuts the flowers.

Sad, Sad Kit Hen

by Amy Helfer
illustrated by Gary Phillips

"Sit on the back deck, Kit.
We can rock, rock, rock, rock."

4

The hat can fit on Kit Hen.
Kit Hen is not sad!

8

Sad Kit Hen can sit, sit.
Ken Cat can sit, sit.

5

Ken Cat met Kit Hen.
Is Kit Hen sick?

2

Kit Hen is not sick.
Kit Hen is a little bit sad.

3

Sad, Sad Kit Hen

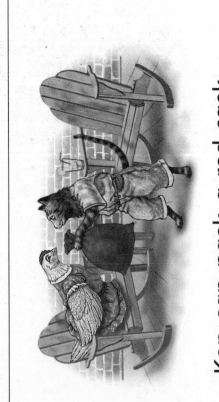

Ken can pack a red sack.
It is for sad Kit Hen.

6

"It is a red hat!" said Kit.
"A red hat in the sack!"

7

Seeds Make Trees

by Olive Jackson   illustrated by Jerry Smath

Dad and Mick said,
"We like trees."

8

Dad said,
"I see seeds.
Do you?"

2

Seeds Make Trees

Mick said,
"Little trees do get big!"

7

Mick said,
"I do!
I see seeds."

Seeds Make Trees

Dad said,
"Little trees get big."

4

Dad said,
"Seeds make little trees."

Seeds Make Trees

5

Mick said,
"I like little trees!"

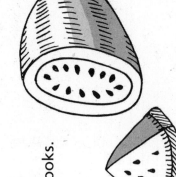

Dear Family Member:

This week we are reading *Seed Secrets*. It tells about plant seeds. It tells that they need water and sun to grow. It tells how seeds travel in the air. I'm learning to check if I understand a book by retelling it in my own words. I can use the pictures in a book to help me remember what I read.

This Week's Skills

Comprehension: retell

High-Frequency Words: here, was

Concept Words: position words

Phonics: U
We can hunt for the letter **u** in magazines, newspapers, and books. I'll help you read the words.

······· (Fold here) ·······

© Macmillan/McGraw-Hill

Name _____

Word Workout

Talk About it

VOCABULARY

observe   seeds

If we buy an avocado in the store, we can put the seed in water and observe how it grows. When it has roots, we can plant it in dirt. (Put three toothpicks in the pit of an avocado to hold it in a glass of water. When it has roots, it can be transferred to a flower pot.)

MY WORDS TO KNOW

High-Frequency Words: here, was

I'm getting sticky notes. On each one write your name followed by the words **was here**! You can put the notes in different places in our home for our family members to find.

Concept Words: position words

in, out, over, under

Let's find a ball and a box. I'll keep moving the ball and you can tell if the ball is **in** or **out** of the box, **over** or **under** the box.

Tell It All!

Let's watch a TV show together. At each commercial break we'll retell what we just heard and saw. I'll help you write sentences. You can draw pictures to help us recall.

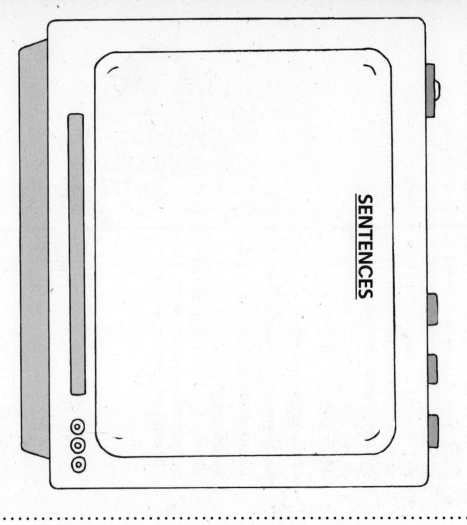

SENTENCES

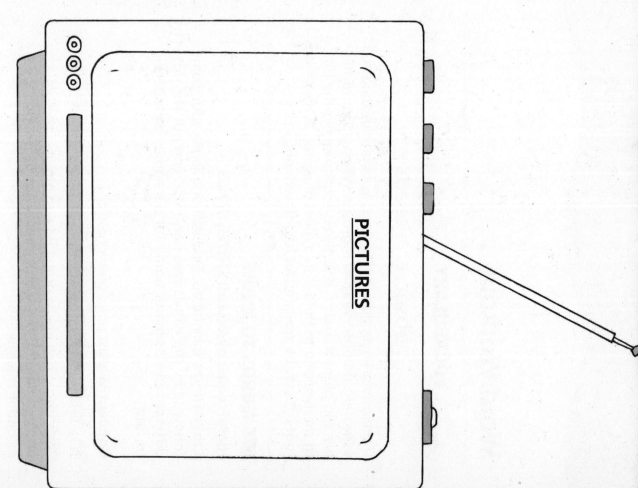

PICTURES

Conexión con el hogar

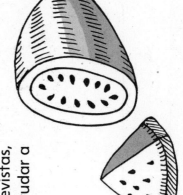

Queridos familiares:

Esta semana estamos leyendo *Seed Secrets*. Trata de las semillas de las plantas. Dice que necesitan agua y sol para crecer. Cuenta cómo las semillas viajan por el aire. Estoy aprendiendo a ver si comprendo un cuento al contarlo con mis propias palabras. Puedo usar las ilustraciones de un libro para recordar lo que leo.

MIS DESTREZAS DE LA SEMANA

Comprensión: volver a contar

Palabras de uso frecuente: here, was

Palabras de concepto: palabras que indican posición

Fonética: U
Vamos a buscar la letra u en revistas, periódicos y libros. Te voy a ayudar a leer las palabras.

Nombre _____

(fold here)

© Macmillan/McGraw-Hill

Ejercicio de palabras

 Talk About it

VOCABULARIO

observe   seeds

Si compramos un aguacate podemos poner la semilla en agua y observar cómo crece. Cuando le crezcan raíces, lo podremos plantar. (Ponga tres palillos en la semilla del aguacate para que se pueda sostener en un vaso de agua. Cuando tenga raíces siembre la semilla en una matera.)

MIS PALABRAS

Palabras de uso frecuente: here, was

Aquí tengo notas adhesivas. Escribe en cada una tu nombre seguido de las palabras *was here*! Luego pon las notas en diferentes lugares de la casa para que las encuentren otros miembros de la familia.

Palabras de concepto: palabras que indican posición
in, out, over, under

Necesitamos una pelota y una caja. Voy a mover la pelota y tú me vas a decir en inglés si la pelota está **in**, **out**, **over** o **under**, o sea *dentro, fuera, sobre o debajo de la caja.*

229

¡Cuéntamelo todo!

Vamos a mirar un programa de televisión juntos. Cada vez que pasen un anuncio nos contaremos lo que acabamos de ver y escuchar. Te ayudaré a escribir oraciones. Tú puedes hacer dibujos que nos ayuden a recordar lo que vimos.

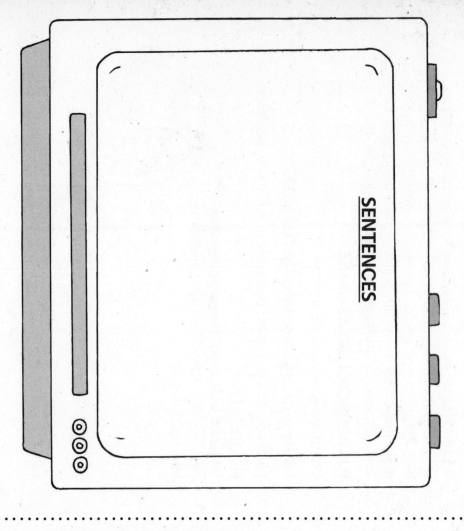

SENTENCES

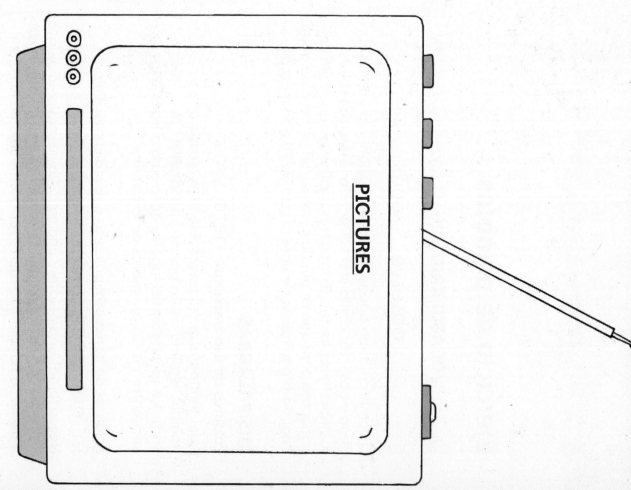

PICTURES

A Bud Is Up

by Mara Debonne
illustrated by Paige Billin-Frye

---

3. Tap it. Tap it in.
4. Water it on top.

4

Nick can see it! Nick did it!
Let the bud pop up, up, up!

8

---

5. Set the cup in back.
Set it in the sun.

5

It is fun, fun, fun.
Nick can do it!

2

3

1. Pick up a cup.
2. Pack it. Fit it in.

A Bud Is Up

But the sun is hot here.
It can pop up, up!

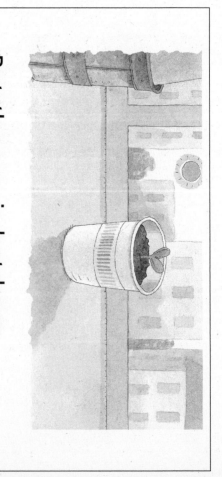

7

It did not pop up.
The sun was not up.

6

From Seed to Plant

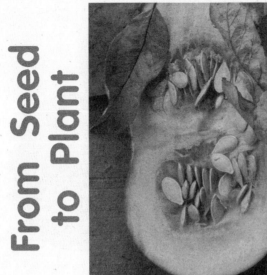

by Bill Williams

We love melon!

8

Here are tomato seeds.

seeds

From Seed to Plant

© 2007 Macmillan/McGraw-Hill

This melon plant was a melon seed.

This tomato plant was a tomato seed.

3

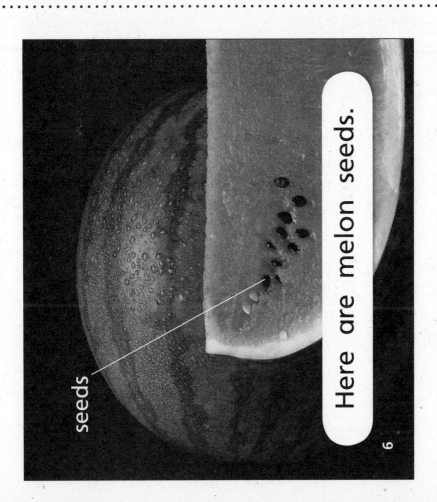

seeds

Here are melon seeds.

6

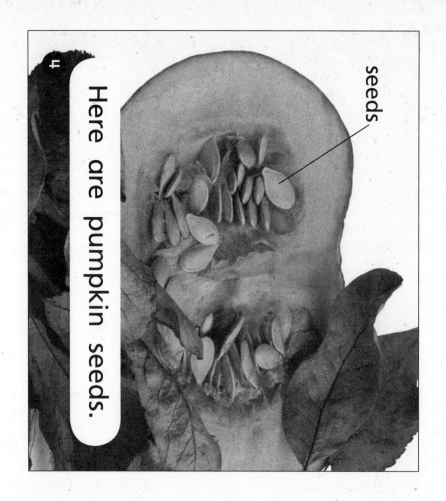

seeds

Here are pumpkin seeds.

4

This pumpkin plant was a pumpkin seed.

5

Home-School Connection

Dear Family Member:

This week we are reading *Sunflower House*, about a boy who plants seeds and watches them grow into big, big, bright yellow flowers. The boy and two friends pretend that the tall flowers are the walls and roof of a house. The house begins to fall at the end of the summer. There is a picture of a seed growing, however. I can figure out that soon a stem will grow and there will be many flowers next summer.

This Week's Skills

Comprehension: draw conclusions

High-Frequency Words:
here, was, and, what, little, said

Concept Words: positional words

Phonics: ot, op, ick
Can you rhyme a word with *got?* Can you rhyme a word with *hop?* What about *pick?*

Name _____

·········· (fold here) ··········

© Macmillan/McGraw-Hill

Word Workout

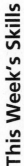
Talk About it

VOCABULARY

garden   senses

We could visit a vegetable garden, look at a picture of one, or close our eyes and picture one. Now we'll use all five senses to talk about the garden. What do you see, hear, smell, feel, and taste?

MY WORDS TO KNOW

High-Frequency Words

here, was, and, what, little, said

I'll write each word on a piece of paper and leave one letter out. Can you fill in the missing letter? I'll help you.

Concept Words:

bottom, in, middle, out, over, top, under

Let's sit at the table and I'll put out a cup and a spoon. I'll give you directions such as: *Put the spoon in the middle of the table.* We can use all the words that way.

Where Are You?

Play a game with your child. Write the numbers one and two on cards, and put the cards in a bag. Use two different coins as markers. Take turns picking a number and moving that many spaces. Tell if you would use the pictured object at school or at the beach. The first one to reach "Stop" wins.

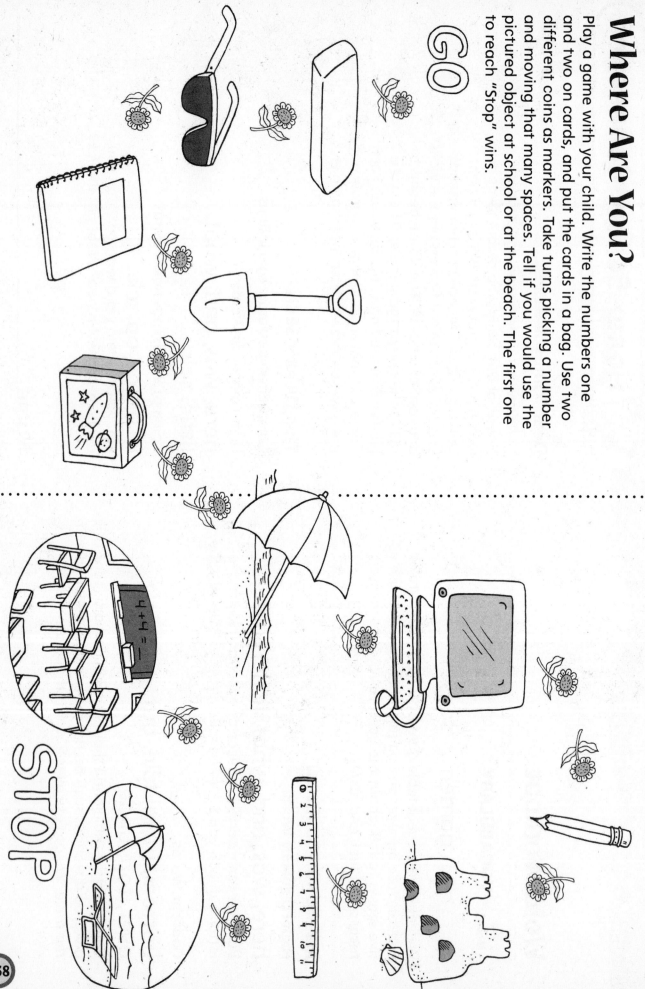

Querios familiares:

Queridos familiares:

Esta semana estamos leyendo *Sunflower House*, acerca de un niño que planta semillas y ve cómo crecen hasta transformarse en grandes y brillantes flores amarillas. El niño y dos amigos más imaginan que las altas flores son las paredes y el techo de una casa. Al final del verano la casa comienza a caerse. Sin embargo, hay una ilustración con una semilla que crece. Me parece que va a crecer un tallo, y que el próximo verano habrá muchas flores amarillas.

MIS DESTREZAS DE LA SEMANA

Comprensión: sacar conclusiones

Palabras de uso frecuente:
here, was, and, what, little, said

Palabras de concepto: palabras que indican posición

Fonética: ot, op, ick ¿Puedes encontrar una palabra que rime con *got*? ¿Y con *hop*? ¿Conoces una palabra que rime con *pick*?

© Macmillan/McGraw-Hill

(Fold here.)

Nombre _____

Ejercicio de palabras

Talk About it

VOCABULARIO

garden   senses

Podemos visitar un jardín, observar una fotografía de uno o cerrar los ojos e imaginárnoslo. Vamos a usar los cinco sentidos para hablar del jardín. ¿Qué ves, escuchas, hueles, tocas y saboreas?

MIS PALABRAS

Palabras de uso frecuente:
here, was, and, what, little, said

Voy a escribir cada palabra pero voy a dejar fuera una letra. ¿Puedes decirme qué letra falta? Yo te ayudaré.

Palabras de concepto:
bottom, in, middle, out, over, top, under

Vamos a la mesa. Tengo una taza y una cuchara. Te voy a dar indicaciones en inglés, como: *"Put the spoon in the middle of the table"*. Usemos todas las palabras de esa manera.

¿Dónde estás?

Juegue este juego con su niño: Escriba los números uno y dos en tarjetas y ponga las tarjetas en una bolsa. Use dos monedas distintas como marcadores. Túrnense para sacar un número y avanzar el número de espacios indicados. Diga si usaría el objeto ilustrado en el casillero en la escuela o en la playa. Gana el primero que llegue a "Stop".

GO

STOP

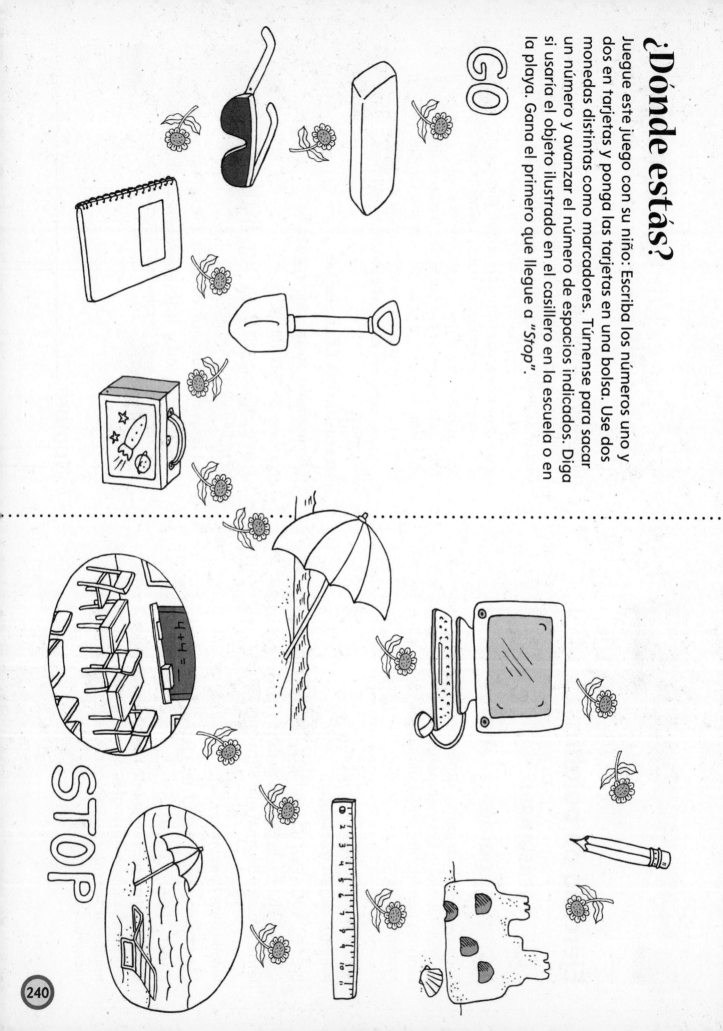

Pick It, Kick It!

by Amy Helfer
illustrated by Nathan Jarvis

"Do not pick it, Nat.
Let it sit."

4

"It is a sick pod, Cam.
Can I pick it?"

5

"I can tip it up a lot.
It can pop up, up, Nat."

8

"It is a red bud, Cam."
"Do not pick it, Nat."

2

"It is not red, Cam.
Can I pick it?"

3

Pick It, Kick It!

"Kick the rock, Cam. Kick it!
I can not pick it up."

7

"Hop to it, Nat.
Pick the sick pod."

6

I Like This Flower

by Marie Stone   illustrated by Brian Cody

Kangaroo said, "I like Little Ant. I like Butterfly. I like Honey Bee."

8

"I like flowers,"
said Little Ant.
"I will sit here."

2

I Like This Flower

7

"I like flowers,"
said Butterfly.
"Little Ant and
I will sit here."

3

I Like This Flower

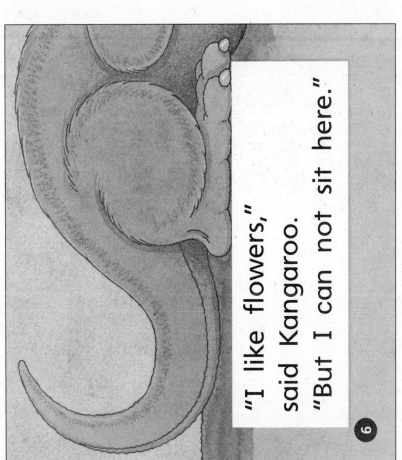

"I like flowers,"
said Kangaroo.
"But I can not sit here."

6

4

"I like flowers,"
said Honey Bee.
"Little Ant, Butterfly,
and I will sit here."

I Like This Flower

5

Click! Click! Click!
"What was that?"
said Little Ant.

Home-School Connection

Dear Family Member:

This week we are reading *Beetles*. Beetles are insects. They have three pairs of legs, three parts to their bodies, and no backbone. A beetle has wings, and most of them can fly. I'm learning how to put things into groups. I figure out how things are alike and how they are different. In this book there are different kinds of beetles. Ladybugs and fireflies are both beetles.

This Week's Skills

Comprehension: classify and categorize

High-Frequency Words: she, he

Concept Words: opposite words

Phonics: g, w
We can look for words that start with the letters **g** and **w** in books you are reading.

Name _____

·····································(fold here)·····································

© Macmillan/McGraw-Hill

Word Workout

Talk About it

VOCABULARY

interesting   insects

Let's talk about insects we have seen. Which one is the most interesting one for you? Tell me about it.

MY WORDS TO KNOW

High-Frequency Words: she, he

I'm going to print the words **she** and **he** on index cards and read them to you. Point to the card with the word as I say each one. Can you write each word? Can you tell me other words that rhyme with **she** and **he**?

Concept Words: opposite words

fast, slow, high, low

When I say *fast* or *slow*, move your body so that it is going either fast or slow. When I say *high* or *low*, point to something up high or down low. Let's repeat this until we use all of the words.

247

Is It an Insect?

We're going to circle each insect in red and underline each mammal in blue. Then you can draw another animal in the empty box. Is it an insect or a mammal?

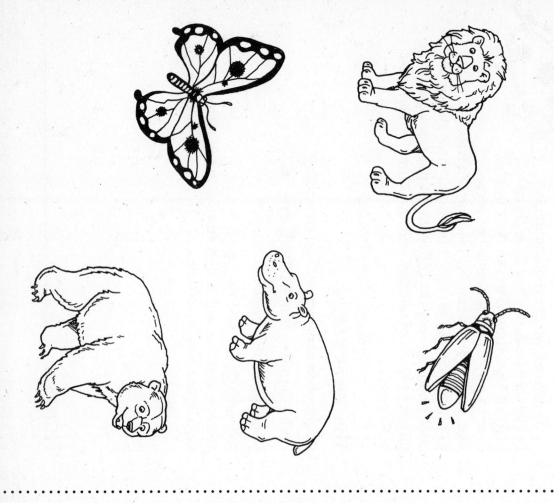

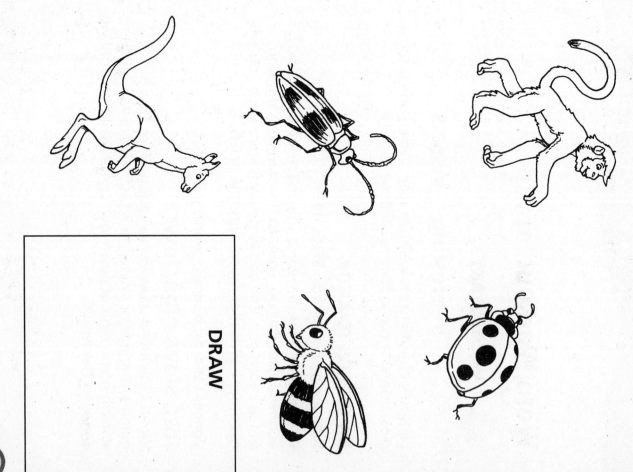

DRAW

Queridos familiares:

Esta semana estamos leyendo *Beetles*. Los *beetles*, que en español se llaman escarabajos, son insectos. Tienen tres pares de patas y su cuerpo tiene tres partes, pero no tienen columna vertebral. Los escarabajos tienen alas, y la mayoría de ellos puede volar. Estoy aprendiendo a poner las cosas en grupos. Observo cómo se parecen y cómo se diferencian para agruparlas. En este libro hay diferentes tipos de escarabajos. Las mariquitas y las luciérnagas son escarabajos también.

MIS DESTREZAS DE LA SEMANA

Comprensión: clasificar y categorizar

Palabras de uso frecuente: she, he

Palabras de concepto: palabras opuestas

Fonética: g, w
Vamos a buscar palabras que comiencen con la letra **g** y con la **w** en los libros que estás leyendo.

Nombre _____

(fold here)

Ejercicio de palabras

VOCABULARIO

interesting   insects

Hablemos de insectos que hemos visto. ¿Cuál es el más interesonte? ¿Por qué?

MIS PALABRAS

Palabras de uso frecuente: she, he

Voy a escribir en dos tarjetas las palabras *she* y *he* en letras de imprenta y las voy a leer. Señala la tarjeta donde está la palabra que escuchas. ¿Puedes escribir *she* y *he*? ¿Puedes decirme otras palabras que rimen con *she* y *he*?

Palabras de concepto: palabras opuestas

fast, slow, high, low

Cuano dijo **fast** o **slow**, mueva el cuerpo al mismo velocidad. Cuando digo **high** o **low**, indica con el dedo algo que es alto o bajo. Vamos a repetir hasta que usamos todas las palabras.

¿Es un insecto?

Vamos a encerrar a cada insecto en un círculo rojo y subrayar en azul a los mamíferos. Después puedes dibujar otro animal en el recuadro vacío. ¿Es un insecto o un mamífero?

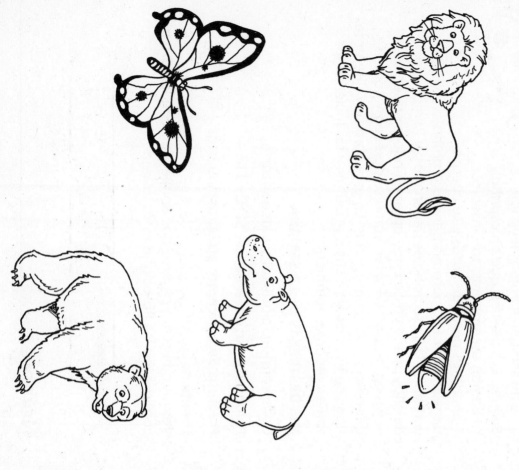

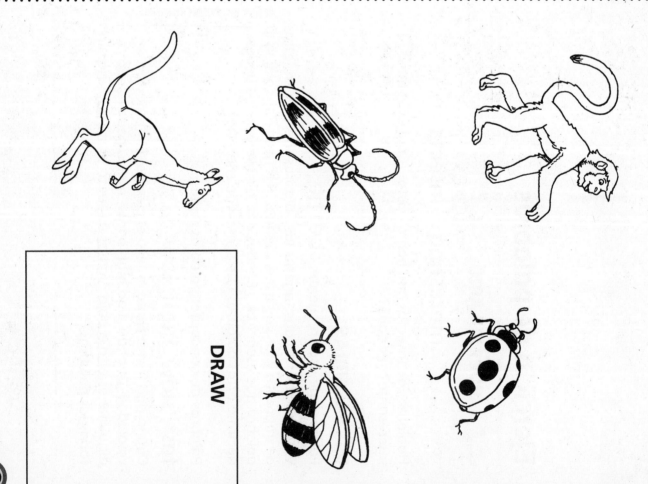

DRAW

Bug in a Web

by Ana Ruiz

Pat Cat can run, run.
Can she get a big bug?

It is a big, big bug.
Rick can hug it!

8

Tip can wag, wag.
Can he dig up a big bug?

5

A web can get a bug.
It is a big, wet web.

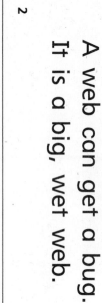

A bug can hop up, up.
Did Tam get it?

Gus can pick up the bug.
It can sit on him.

Bug in a Web

It is not a big bug.
Can Ron see it?

Insects

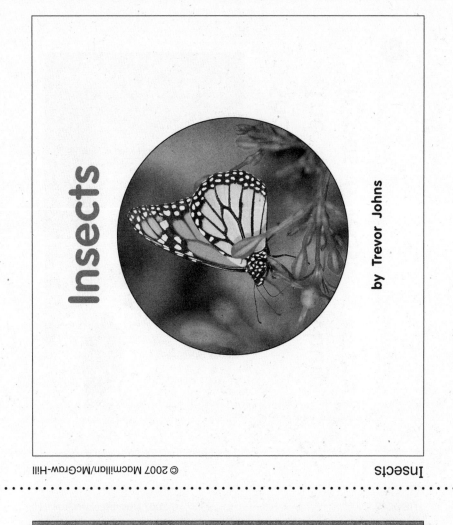

by Trevor Johns

This bug is a spider.
A spider has 8 legs.
Is a spider an insect?

8

She sees a bug.
The bug is a ladybug.
It has 6 legs.

Insects

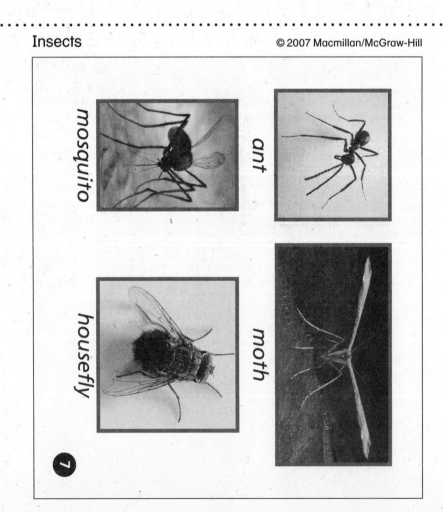

mosquito

ant

housefly

moth

She sees a bug.
The bug is a bee.
It has 6 legs.

3

stick insect

beetle

If a bug has 6 legs,
we say it is an insect!

6

He sees a bug.
The bug is a butterfly.
It has 6 legs.

4

He sees a bug, too.
This bug is a grasshopper.
It has 6 legs.

5

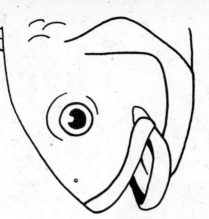

Dear Family Member:

This week we are reading *Fish Faces*. Fish are different shapes, sizes, and colors. They can be spotted, dotted, or striped. Their noses might be long and they might shine. I'm learning how the fish in the book are the same and how they are different.

This Week's Skills

Comprehension: compare and contrast

High-Frequency Words: has, look

Concept Words: opposite words

Phonics: X, V
Let's hunt for words that end with the letter **x** or begin with the letter **v**. We can look in books and magazines.

Name _____

(fold here)

© Macmillan/McGraw-Hill

Word Workout

 Talk About it

VOCABULARY

amazing   ocean

Have we ever been to the ocean? Or have we seen pictures of the ocean? Let's talk about the amazing animals that live there.

MY WORDS TO KNOW

High-Frequency Words: has, look

Write each word on an index card and read it aloud. Have your child copy each word by writing it. Tell your child to say each letter while writing. Repeat. Then your child can "erase" each word and write it from memory.

Concept Words: opposite words

short, long, fat, thin, narrow, wide

Let's make a chart using the words **short, long, fat, thin, narrow,** and **wide**. I'll write the words at the top of the page, and make a column for each word. You can fill in each column with names of things that are **short, long, fat, thin, narrow,** and **wide**.

Fishy Friends

Look at the two fish. Let's talk about how they are alike and how they are different. Then you can color them in.

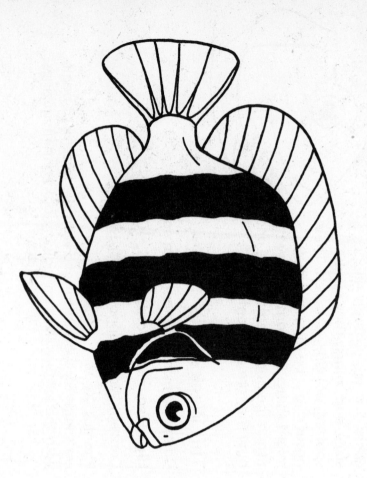

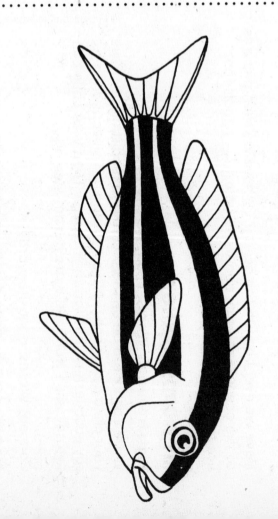

Which fish do you like best? Why?

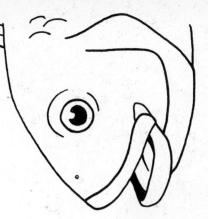

Queridos familiares:

Esta semana estamos leyendo *Fish Faces*. Los peces son de diferentes formas, tamaños y colores. Pueden tener manchas, lunares o rayas. Pueden tener narices largas y pueden brillar. Estoy aprendiendo en qué se parecen los peces del libro y en qué se diferencian.

MIS DESTREZAS DE LA SEMANA

Comprensión: comparar y contrastar

Palabras de uso frecuente: has, look

Palabras de concepto: palabras opuestas

Fonética: X, V

Vamos a buscar palabras que terminen con la letra **x** o comiencen con la letra **v**. Vamos a buscar en libros y revistas.

Nombre _____

(fold here)

© Macmillan/McGraw-Hill

Ejercicio de palabras

Talk About it

VOCABULARIO

amazing   ocean

¿Has estado alguna vez en el océano? ¿Has visto fotos del océano? ¿Has visto fotos del océano? Vamos a hablar de los asombrosos animales que podemos encontrar allí.

MIS PALABRAS

Palabras de uso frecuente: has, look

Escriba cada palabra en una tarjeta y léala en voz alta. Haga que su niño copie cada palabra y que diga cada letra en voz alta a medida que la vaya escribiendo. Repita el procedimiento. Después el niño puede "borrar" las palabras y escribirlas de memoria.

Palabras de concepto: palabras opuestas

short, long, fat, thin, narrow, wide

Vamós a hacer un cuadro y usamos las palabras **short, long, fat, thin, narrow y wide**. Voy a escribir las palabras al alto de la página, y hacer un columna para cada palabra. Puedes escribir en cada columna los nombres de cosas que son **short, long, fat, thin, narrow y wide**.

259

Peces amigos

Observa los dos peces. ¿En qué se parecen y en qué se diferencian? Después podrás colorearlos.

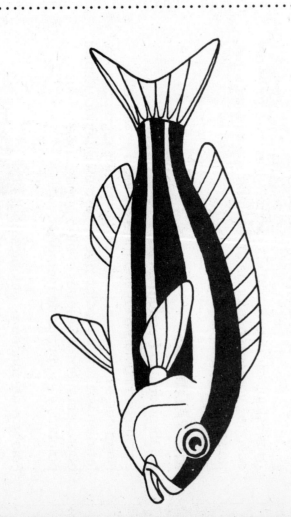

Which fish do you like best? Why?

A Vet Can Fix It!

by Liz Ray

Look at Big Pig!
Is Big Pig sick?

Pat is a wet vet!
Pat can fix it.

A sick pet is not fun.
A vet can fix it!

Red Fox can not run.
It has a bad back leg.

Ed is a vet.
Ed can fix a sick fox.

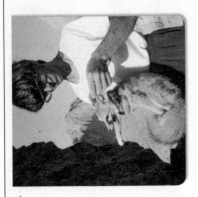

A Vet Can Fix It!

Sick Rex is in the van.
Can a vet fix Rex?

Jack Duck had bad luck.
Peg can fix Jack Duck.

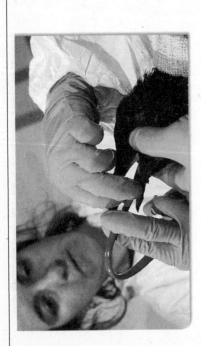

Down in the Ocean

by Michael Evans

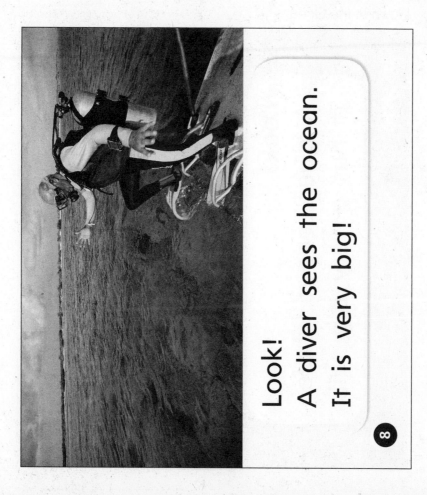

Look!
A diver sees the ocean.
It is very big!

8

2

Look!
A diver sees the ocean.
The diver jumps in.

7

Look!
A diver sees a whale.
It has a very big tail.

Down in the Ocean

Look!
A diver sees a turtle.
It has a very big shell.

3

Look!
A diver sees an octopus.
It has very big arms.

4

Look!
A diver sees a fish.
It has big eyes.

Look!
A diver sees a shark.
It has a big mouth.

5

Dear Family Member:

This week we are reading *If the Dinosaurs Came Back*. The boy in the book thinks of all the ways dinosaurs could be helpful. For example, lots of people could ride them to work. I'm learning that some stories are about things that could not really happen. A boy could really love dinosaurs, but they couldn't come back, and they couldn't take people to work!

This Week's Skills

Comprehension: fantasy and reality

High-Frequency Words: she, he, has, look

Concept Words: opposite words

Phonics: et, ot, ox, ix, ed, en
Can you think of rhymes for these words: *pet, dot, fox, fix, bed, ten?*

Name _____

(fold here)

© Macmillan/McGraw-Hill

Word Workout

Talk About It

VOCABULARY

fantasy   reality

Let's change one of your experiences just a little bit so that it becomes a fantasy. You might say that your friend the dinosaur sits next to you on the bus.

MY WORDS TO KNOW

High-Frequency Words: she, he, has, look

Say each word in random order. Have your child point to each one. Finally, have your child copy the words into columns of words with two letters, three letters, and four letters.

Concept Words: opposite words

big, small, short, tall, fat, thin, high, low, loud, quiet, fast, slow

I am going to write down the words **big, small, short, tall, fat, thin, high, low, loud, quiet, fast, slow** on cards. You can draw a picture on the card that matches the word. Then we'll shuffle the cards and match each word with its opposite.

Get Real

We need two small objects for markers, such as a raisin and a piece of macaroni. We'll put them on the ship that says GO. Flip a coin. Move one space for "heads" or two spaces for "tails." Whenever you land on a picture, tell whether the picture shows fantasy or reality. We can take turns. Whoever gets to the treasure chest first wins!

Queridos familiares:

Esta semana estamos leyendo *If the Dinosaurs Came Back*. El niño del libro piensa en todas las maneras en que los dinosaurios podrían ayudarnos. Por ejemplo, mucha gente podría montarse en ellos para ir al trabajo.

Estoy aprendiendo que algunos cuentos tratan de cosas que no podrían suceder en la realidad. A un niño le pueden encantar los dinosaurios, pero no pueden regresar ni tampoco llevar a la gente al trabajo.

MIS DESTREZAS DE LA SEMANA

Comprensión: fantasía y realidad

Palabras de uso frecuente: she, he, has, look

Palabras de concepto: palabras opuestas

Fonética: et, ot, ox, ix, ed, en
¿Pueden pensar en palabras que rimen con las siguientes: *pet, dot, fox, fix, bed, ten?*

Nombre _____

······· (Fold here) ·······

© Macmillan/McGraw-Hill

Ejercicio de palabras

 Talk About it

VOCABULARIO

fantasy   reality

Vamos a cambiar una de tus experiencias, sólo un poquito, para que se vuelva fantasía. Me podrías contar, por ejemplo, que tu amigo el dinosaurio se sienta junto a ti en el autobús.

MIS PALABRAS

Palabras de uso frecuente: she, he, has, look

Diga las palabras al azar. Haga que su niño señale cada una cuando la escuche. Finalmente haga que el niño copie las palabras en columnas, una de palabras con dos letras, otra de tres letras y otra de cuatro.

Palabras de concepto: palabras opuestas

big, small, short, tall, fat, thin, high, low, loud, quiet, fast, slow

Voy a escribir las palabras **big, small, short, tall, fat, thin, high, low, loud, quiet, fast, slow** en tarjetas. Puedes dibujar un dibujo en la tarjeta que corresponde con la palabra. Luego vamos a barajar las tarjetas y a emparejar cada palabra con su opuesto.

¿Realidad o fantasía?

Necesitamos dos objetos pequeños como una pasa de uva y un trozo de macarrón para hacer de marcadores. Los vamos a poner en el barco marcado "Go" y a echar una moneda. Avanzamos un espacio si sale "Cara" y dos si sale "Seca". Debemos observar la ilustración del lugar donde caemos y decir si muestra una fantasía o algo que podría suceder en la realidad. Vamos a turnarnos. Gana el que llegue primero al cofre del tesoro.

Pat and the Vet

by Amy Helfer

illustrated by Nathan Jarvis

Dad got a big tan box.
It had a red pad in it.

4

Dad ran to get the van.
Pat got in.

5

Pat ran up to Tip.
Tip got a big, big hug!

8

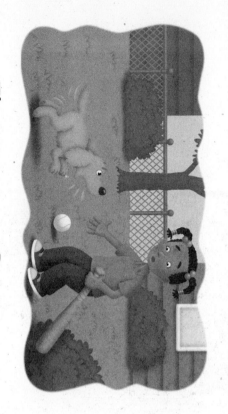

Tip ran up to Pat.
Tip did not wag!

2

Tip led Pat to a sick cat.
The cat did not get up.

3

Pat and the Vet

Pat sat in back.
The sick cat sat in back.

6

Meg the vet had a look.
Meg did fix it!

7

Big Ben

by Susie Fineman   illustrated by John Kanzler

Horse said, "Shhhhh.
Look in the box."

8

Big Ben did not
see Little Sheep.
"I will look for
Little Sheep," he said.

Big Ben © 2007 Macmillan/McGraw-Hill

Big Ben ran to see Horse.
"Has Little Sheep come
here?" he said.

Big Ben ran to see Cow.
"Has Little Sheep come
here?" he said.

3

Pig said, "No.
Is she with Horse?
Look in the barn."

6

Cow said, "No.
Is she with Pig?
Look in the pen."

4

Big Ben ran to see Pig.
"Has Little Sheep come
here?" he said.

5

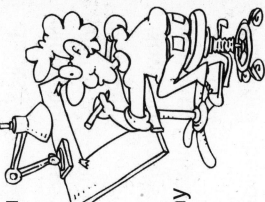

Dear Family Member:

This week we are reading *What Do You Know!* The words in the book rhyme, and I can look for things in the pictures that the words name. I look for shapes, fruits, colors, and animals. I'm learning how to use the pictures in a book to help me understand it.

This Week's Skills

Comprehension: use illustrations

High-Frequency Words: with, my

Concept Words: food words

Phonics: j, qu

Get out some of your books and we can hunt for words that begin with the letters j and qu.

Name _____

····· (fold here) ·····

© Macmillan/McGraw-Hill

Word Workout

Talk About it

VOCABULARY

understand   describe

Look at a picture in a book. Describe the picture for me. Tell me what you understand from looking at the picture.

MY WORDS TO KNOW

High-Frequency Words: with, my

I'm going to write the words with and my on a piece of paper. We can read the words together. Finger-trace each word as we say the letters. Can you write the words from memory now?

Concept Words:

beans, blueberries, cherries, greens, salad

I'm writing *fruit* on one half of a piece of paper, and *vegetable* on the other half. When I give you a word, tell me if it names a fruit or vegetable. Then you can draw a picture for the word on the correct half of the paper.

Count and Color

In this game, I'll ask you questions and give you directions. You can answer them and follow them by looking at the big picture.

How many ducks do you see? Color the ducks yellow.

How many pigs do you see? Color the pigs pink.

How many cats do you see? Color the cats gray.

Add three balloons.

Add one more cat.

Color the merry-go-round horses different colors.

Let's make up a story about the picture.

Queridos familiares:

Esta semana estamos leyendo *What Do You Know!*
Las palabras del libro riman, y puedo buscar en las ilustraciones cosas a las que se refieren las palabras. Busco formas, frutas, colores y animales. Estoy aprendiendo a usar las ilustraciones de un libro para comprenderlo.

MIS DESTREZAS DE LA SEMANA

Comprensión: usar ilustraciones

Palabras de uso frecuente: With, my

Palabras de concepto: palabras de comida

Fonética: j, qu
Saca algunos de tus libros. Vamos a buscar palabras que comiencen con las letras j y qu.

Nombre _____

- - - - - - - - - - - - - (fold here) - - - - - - - - - - - - -

© Macmillan/McGraw-Hill

Ejercicio de palabras

Talk About it

VOCABULARIO

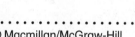
understand   describe

Mira una de las ilustraciones de un libro. Descríbemela. Dime qué es lo que entiendes de la ilustración.

MIS PALABRAS

Palabras de uso frecuente: With, my

Voy a escribir las palabras with y my en un papel. Podemos leerlas juntos. Traza con un dedo las letras a medida que las vayamos diciendo. No mires las palabras, ¿puedes escribirlas de memoria?

Palabras de concepto:

beans, blueberries, cherries, greens, salad

Voy a escribir *fruit* en la mitad de un trozo de papel, y *vegetable* en la otra mitad. Cuando diga una palabra debes decirme si es una fruta o un vegetal. Después puedes hacer un dibujo de la palabra en la mitad del papel que corresponda.

Cuenta y colorea

En este juego te voy a hacer preguntas y dar indicaciones.
Mira la ilustración grande para contestar las preguntas.

How many ducks do you
see? Color the ducks
yellow.

How many pigs do
you see? Color the
pigs pink.

How many cats do you
see? Color the cats
gray.

Add three balloons.

Add one more cat.

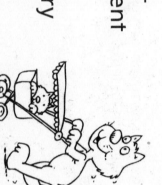

Color the merry-go-
round horses different
colors.

Let's make up a story
about the picture.

Jeb Is Quick!

by Anita Faulk
illustrated by Erin Mauterer

4

Jen can tap, tap, tap.
Jen can kick, kick, kick.

Jeb Is Quick!

Jack can quack.
Is Jack a little duck?

5

Bob is back!
Bob did not quit.

8

Jeb Is Quick!

I am Jeb.
I am a big, quick jet!

2

Jim can jig.
Jim can jig with Deb.

3

Kim got my red jug.
Kim is quick!

7

Bob can jog.
But Bob is hot!

9

Duck Quacks

by Katherine Scraper   illustrated by Robin Oz

"Quack!" said Duck.
"I am fun and I
can quack!"

8

"Can you quack?"
said Jen.
"Ack!" said Duck.

2

"My duck is fun,"
said Jen.
"I am not sad."

7

"Ack?" said Jen.
"I am sad.
My duck can
not quack."

"My duck can juggle
with me!" said Jen.

"My duck can skate with me!" said Jen.

4

Duck Quacks

"My duck can dance with me!" said Jen.

5

Dear Family Member:

This week we are reading *Warthogs Paint: a Messy Color Book*. One rainy day, the warthogs decide to paint their kitchen wall. First they paint red, then yellow, then blue. I'm learning that when one thing happens in a story, it makes something else happen. In this book, the warthogs mix blue paint with yellow paint. Then they have green paint.

This Week's Skills

Comprehension: identify cause and effect

High-Frequency Words: me, where

Concept Words: sound words

Phonics: y, z

How many words can you name that begin with the letters **y** or **z**? I'll give you hints, such as: *This looks like a horse but it has black and white stripes.* I'll print the words to name. You can point to the letter in each word and name it. Then we can say the words together. *(zebra, zipper, zero, zigzag, yard, yawn, year, yellow)*

© Macmillan/McGraw-Hill

(fold here)

Name _____

Word Workout

Talk About it

VOCABULARY

imagine   create

Imagine a beautiful picture. How would you create it? What would you put in the painting? What colors would you use?

MY WORDS TO KNOW

High-Frequency Words: me, where

Your child can use a finger to write the words **me** and **where** on your back as you name the letters. Then have your child write the words on paper. You might pin the word **me** on yourself for your child to see.

Concept Words: sound words

buzz, boom, splash, zoom

Let's pretend to be a bee, a thunder cloud, a duck, and a jet. We'll act out being each thing, while we make the sound that matches it. We'll use sound words like: **buzz, boom, splash, zoom.**

Tic Tac Toe

Let's read the causes below. We'll take turns telling what will happen. After each turn, you can mark an **X** on the tic-tac-toe board, and I'll mark an **O**. Whoever gets three in a row first wins! We may not need to use all the clues. We can make up our own clues and play again.

You step in a puddle.

Your feet grow.

You have new skates.

Your phone rings.

You hear a funny joke.

You jump into a pool.

You are very thirsty.

You are very tired.

You get a new baseball.

Your dog is hungry.

You feel sick.

Your dad gets a pizza.

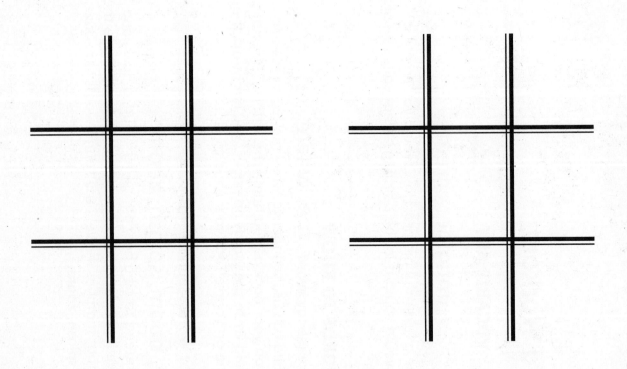

Queridos familiares:

Esta semana estamos leyendo *Warthogs Paint: a Messy Color Book*. Un día de lluvia los jabalíes deciden pintar la pared de su cocina. Primero la pintan de color rojo, luego de amarillo y finalmente de azul. Estoy aprendiendo que algo que pasa en un cuento hace que pase otra cosa. En este libro los jabalíes mezclan pintura azul con pintura amarilla. Entonces terminan teniendo pintura verde.

MIS DESTREZAS DE LA SEMANA

Comprensión: identificar causa y efecto

Palabras de uso frecuente: me, where

Palabras de concepto: palabras de sonido

Fonética: y, z

¿Cuántas palabras en inglés me puedes decir que comiencen con y o con z? Una pista: *Parece un caballo, pero tiene franjas blancas y negras (zebra)*. Voy a escribir las palabras que tú me digas. Señala las letras **y** y **z** y dilas. Luego digamos las palabras juntos. *(zebra, zipper, zero, zigzag, yard, yawn, year, yellow)*

Nombre _____

(fold here)

© Macmillan/McGraw-Hill

Ejercicio de palabras

 Talk About It

VOCABULARIO

imagine   create

Imagina que haces una hermosa ilustración. ¿Cómo la crearías? ¿Qué pondrías en la ilustración? ¿Qué colores usarías?

MIS PALABRAS

Palabras de uso frecuente: me, where

Su niño puede escribir con un dedo las palabras *me* y *where* en su espalda a medida que usted vaya diciendo cada letra. Luego haga que el niño escriba las palabras en un papel. Si usted quiere, puede prenderse el papel con la palabra *me* para que su niño la vea.

Palabras de concepto: palabras de sonido

buzz, boom, splash, zoom

Nos imaginamos a ester una abeja, un nubarrón, un pato y un avión. Vamos a fingir cada cosa y hacemos el sonido que le corresponde. Vamos a usar palabras de sonido como: **buzz, boom, splash, zoom.**

289

Ta te ti

Vamos a leer la lista de causas de abajo. Vamos a turnarnos para decir qué pasará después. Al terminar tu turno, escribirás una **X** en el tablero; yo escribiré una **O**. Gana el primero que tenga tres marcas en una hilera. Puede que no necesitemos usar todas las pistas. Después podemos crear nuestras propias pistas y jugar otra vez.

You step in a puddle.

Your feet grow.

You have new skates.

Your phone rings.

You hear a funny joke.

You jump into a pool.

You are very thirsty.

You are very tired.

You get a new baseball.

Your dog is hungry.

You feel sick.

Your dad gets a pizza.

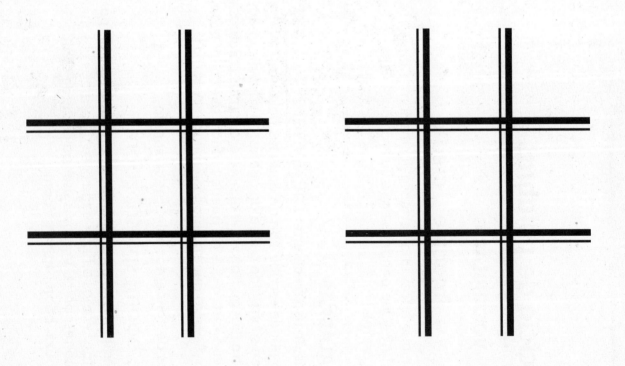

Zip? Zig Zag? Yes!

by Maureen Stiles

photographed by Ken O'Donoghue

I am Kim.
I got a big, tan yam.

4

It is a big, hot yam.
Yum, yum, yum!

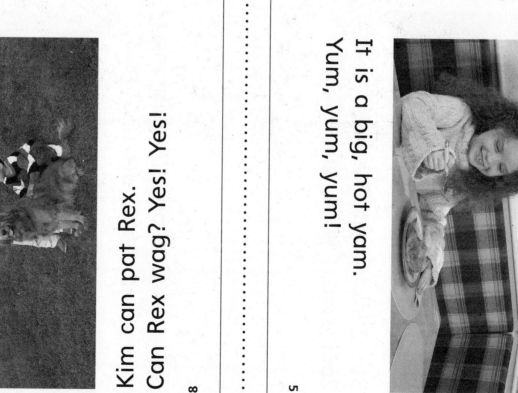

5

Kim can pat Rex.
Can Rex wag? Yes! Yes!

8

Rex can zip, zip, zip.
Where can Rex run a lap?

3

I am Zack.
Rex is my big dog.

2

Zip? Zig Zag? Yes!

But Zack is not like me.
Zack said, "Yuck, yuck!"

6

Zack can zip, zip, zip.
But Kim can zig zag.

7

My Pet and Me

by Tyler Martin

My pet is at the zoo!

8

2

This is my pet.
If I run,
my pet will run too.

This is the pet I want.
Can you see where
my pet is?

7

This is my pet too.
Can you see where
his name is?

3

This is me.
I do not
have a pet yet.

6

This is my pet.
If I let my pet go,
it will run.

This is my pet too.
Can you see where
his name is?

Squeaky

5

Dear Family Member:

This week we are reading *Turtle Splash! Countdown at the Pond*. The book begins with ten turtles, until a bullfrog scares them. One turtle jumps into the pond. All the pictures show what the pond looks like.

This Week's Skills

Comprehension: setting

High-Frequency Words:
me, where, with, my, has, look

Concept Words: number words

Phonics: up, ut, un
Can you think of two words that end with the sound *up*? (*cup, pup*) How about words that end with the sound *ut*? (*but, cut, nut*) How about *un*? (*fun, run, sun*)

Name _____

·····(fold here)·····

Word Workout

 Talk About it

VOCABULARY

explore   curious

What are you curious about? Is there someplace you would like to explore? What would you see there?

MY WORDS TO KNOW

High-Frequency Words:
me, where, with, my, has, look

Let's read the words above. Look for those words in books, and when we go outside we can look for them on signs. You can finger-write each word on my hand as you name the letters.

Concept Words:
eight, five, four, nine, one, seven, six, three, two

I'm going to write each number word on an index card. We can read the words together. Then I'll hold up each card and you can make that many dots below each word.

Where Is It?

We can play "Where Is It?" We need two small markers, such as a raisin and a piece of macaroni. We each place our marker on one of the frogs. First, flip a coin. Move to the first picture for "heads" or the second picture for "tails." Tell me what the setting is. We'll take turns. Whoever gets to the pond first wins! We can play again.

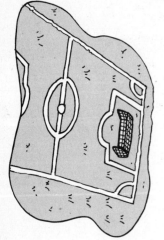

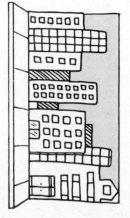

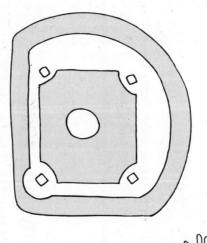

Conexión con el hogar

Queridos familiares:

Esta semana leeremos *Turtle Splash! Countdown at the Pond*. El libro comienza con diez tortugas, hasta que un sapo enorme las asusta. Una de las tortugas se zambulle en la laguna. Estoy aprendiendo que los cuentos pueden ocurrir en distintos lugares y en épocas diferentes. En todas las ilustraciones del libro aparece la laguna, y me puedo imaginar muy bien cómo sería si yo estuviera allí.

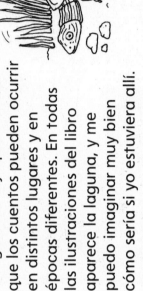

MIS DESTREZAS DE LA SEMANA

Comprensión: el ambiente

Palabras de uso frecuente:

me, where, with, my, has, look

Palabras de concepto: numerales

Fonética: up, ut, un

¿Puedes pensar en dos palabras que terminen con el sonido *up*? (*cup, pup*). ¿Y que terminen con el sonido *ut*? (*but, cut, nut*). ¿Y con el sonido *un*? (*fun, run, sun*).

Nombre _____

·······(Fold here)·······

© Macmillan/McGraw-Hill

Ejercicio de palabras

Talk About it

VOCABULARIO

explore   curious

¿Qué te despierta la curiosidad? ¿Hay algún lugar que te gustaría explorar? ¿Qué podrías ver allí?

MIS PALABRAS

Palabras de uso frecuente:

me, where, with, my, has, look

Vamos a leer las palabras de arriba. Búscalas en libros, y cuando salgamos búscalas en carteles. Escribe cada palabra en mi mano con un dedo mientras dices las letras.

Palabras de concepto:

eight, five, four, nine, one, seven, six, three, two

Voy a escribir cada una de las palabras en una tarjeta. Leamos las palabras juntos. Luego voy a darte las tarjetas y tú podrás dibujar en cada una la cantidad de puntos que el número indique.

¿Dónde está?

Podemos jugar a "¿Dónde está?" Necesitamos dos marcadores pequeños, como una pasa de uva y un trozo de macarrón. Cada uno coloca su marcador en uno de-los sapos. Después lanzamos una moneda. Avanza a la primera ilustración si sacas *heads*, y a la segunda si sacas *tails*. Dime cuál es el ambiente. Nos turnaremos. Gana el primero que llegue a la laguna. Juguemos otra vez.

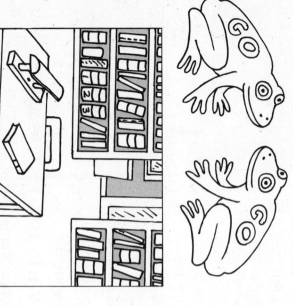

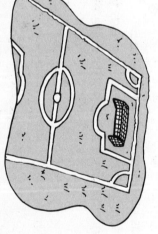

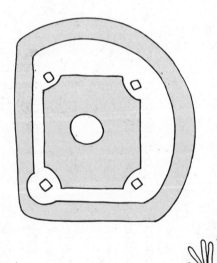

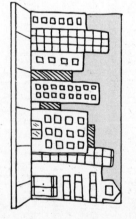

Yes, Tip! Tug!

by Amy Helfer

illustrated by Nathan Jarvis

It is fun to tug on it.
Tug, tug, tug!

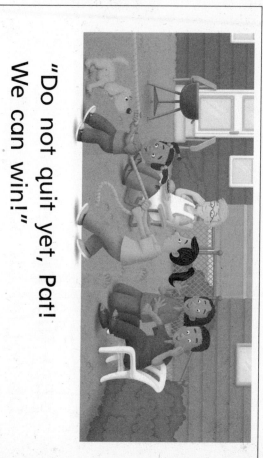

4

"Do not quit yet, Pat!
We can win!"

5

Tip, Cam, and Pat win!
Tip is a fun pup!

8

Yes, Tip! Tug!

Cam got a fat rope.
"Can we tug on it?"

2

Pat ran up to Cam.
Sam, Nat, and Pam ran up.

3

"Zip! Tug! Dig in!
Do not let up on this job."

6

Tip got in back.
Tip can tug! Tug, Tip!

7

Can You Count?

by Olive Jackson   illustrated by Priscilla Burris

Jack said, "That was quick!"

"Count with me," said Fox.

8

"Where is Turtle?" said Jack.

"Here I am," said Turtle.

Can You Count? © 2007 Macmillan/McGraw-Hill

"Can you count
to ten?" said Jack.

Fox said, "Yes. My
mom counts like this."

2, 4, 6,
8, 10

3

"Can you count to ten?" said Jack.

"Yes, I can," said Turtle.

"Count with me."

"Where is Fox?" said Jack.

"Here I am," said Fox.

"Where is Zebra?" said Jack.
"Here I am," said Zebra.

4

"Can you count to ten?" said Jack.
"Yes, I can," said Zebra.
"Count with me."

1, 2, 3, 4,
5, 6, 7, 8,
9, 10

5

Calendar

Monday	Tuesday	Wednesday	Thursday	Friday

Name _____

Calendar

© Macmillan/McGraw-Hill

Monday	Tuesday	Wednesday	Thursday	Friday

Name _____

Calendar

Monday	Tuesday	Wednesday	Thursday	Friday

Name _____

Calendar

Monday	Tuesday	Wednesday	Thursday	Friday

Name _____

Calendar

Monday	Tuesday	Wednesday	Thursday	Friday

Name _____

Calendar

Name _____

Monday	Tuesday	Wednesday	Thursday	Friday

Calendar

Monday	Tuesday	Wednesday	Thursday	Friday

Name _____

Calendar

Name _____

Monday	Tuesday	Wednesday	Thursday	Friday

Calendar

Monday	Tuesday	Wednesday	Thursday	Friday

Name _____

Calendar

Monday

Tuesday

Wednesday

Thursday

Friday

Name

Credits

▲ **Unit I Week I** *My Mitten*
Cover: Barbara Sitzer/PhotoEdit, Inc. I: Barbara Sitzer/PhotoEdit, Inc.
2: MaryKate Denny/PhotoEdit, Inc. 3: David Young-Wolff/PhotoEdit.Inc.
4: thislife pictures/Alamy. 5: Myrleen Ferguson Cate/PhotoEdit, Inc.
6: Richard Hutchings/PhotoEdit,Inc. 7: Ariel Skelley/CORBIS. 8: Laura
Dwight/CORBIS.

● **Unit I Week I** *We can*
photo credits: Cover, I: Barbara Sitzer/ PhotoEdit, Inc. 2: MaryKate
Denny/PhotoEdit, Inc. 3: David Young-Wolff/PhotoEdit, Inc. 4: thislife
pictures/Alamy. 5: Myrleen Ferguson Cate/PhotoEdit, Inc. 6: Richard
Hutchings/PhotoEdit, Ind 7: Ariel Skelley/CORBIS. 8: Laura Dwight/
CORBIS.

▲ **Unit 2 Week I** *We Like Sam*
Cover, I: ©George Shelley/Masterfile. 2: Rolf Bruderer/CORBIS.
3: Paul Barton/CORBIS. 4: Onne van der Wal/CORBIS. 5: Michael
Keller/CORBIS. 6: David Young-Wolff/PhotoEdit, Inc. 7: Gerhard Steiner/
CORBIS. 8: George Shelley/Masterfile.

● **Unit 2 Week 2** *We Can Share*
photo credits: Cover: Brian Sytnyk/Masterfile; I: Regine Mahaux/Getty
Images; 2: Mitch Diamond/Alamy; 3: Ryan McVay/Getty Images; 4-5: Brian
Sytnyk/Masterfile; 6: Regine Mahaux/Getty Images; 7: G. Baden/Masterfile;
8: Bob Daemmrich/The Image Works.

▲ **Unit 3 Week 2** *It Can Go, Go, Go!*
Cover: (c) David Young-Wolff/Photo Edit. I: ©BananaStock/Alamy.
2: R. Holz/Masterfile. 3: Tony Freeman/Photo Edit. 4: J. David Andrews/
Masterfile. 5: Tom Stewart/CORBIS. 6: PhotoDisc/Getty Images.
7: Kwame Zikomo/SuperStock. 8: Eastcott/Momatiuk/The Image Works.

● **Unit 3 Week 2** *Fast Or Slow?*
photo credits: Cover: John Foxx/ImageState RF/AGE Fotostock;
I: Larry Williams/Corbis; 2: Kim Karpeles/Alamy; 3: Jane Sapinsky/Corbis;
4: Michael Kim/Corbis; 5: Transtock /Alamy; 6: John Foxx/ImageState
RF/AGE Fotostock; 7: Larry Williams/Corbis; 8: Mark M. Lawrence/ Corbis.

▲ **Unit 4 Week I** *Tap It, Nan Min!*
Cover, 1–8: Ken O'Donoghue.

● **Unit 4 Week I** *We Pick Food!*
photo credits Cover: Comstock; I: David Allan Brandt/Getty Images;
2: Nancy Sheehan/Photo Edit; 3: C Squared Studios/ Getty Images;
4-5: Comstock; 6: David Allan Brandt/Getty Images; 7: John A. Rizzo/Getty
Images; 8: Jeff Greenberg/The Image Works.

▲ **Unit 4, Week 2** *We Can!*
Cover, I: Tom Rosenthal/SuperStock. 2: Darren Modricker/CORBIS.
3: Pinto/Masterfile. 4: Tony Cordoza/Photonica. 5: Roy Morsch/CORBIS.
6: plainpicture/Alamy. 7, 8: Elizabeth Knox/Masterfile

● **Unit 4 Week 2** *Let's Have Dinner*
photo credits: Cover: Marcus Lyon/Getty Images; I: C Squared Studios/
Getty Images; 2: Jamie Grill/AGE Fotostock; 3: C Squared Studios/Getty
Images; 4: Ariel Skelley/CORBIS; 5: Lucille Khornak/AGE Fotostock;
6: F. Rombout/AGE Fotostock; 7: Ma rcus Lyon/Getty Images; 8: Banana
Stock/Alamy Images.

● **Unit 4 Week 3** *Thanksgiving*
photo credits: Cover: Michael Newman/Photo Edit; I: Larry Dale Gordon/
Getty Images; 2: Michael Newman/Photo Edit; 3: Jose Luis Pelaez,
Inc./Corbis; 4: Larry Dale Gordon/Getty Images; 5: Vieussens/Alamy;

▲ **Unit 5, Week I** *Sit On It*
Cover: VCL/Getty Images. I: Adam Jones/Visuals Unlimited. 2: Greg
Vaughn/Getty Images. 3: Martin Rugner/Age Fotostock. 4: Mary Clay/Getty
Images. 5: PhotoDisc/Getty Images. 6: Adam Jones/Visuals Unlimited.
7: Ray Coleman/Photo Researchers. 8: David Nardini/Masterfile.

● **Unit 5 Week I** *Animals in Nature*
Photo credits Cover: Ruth Cole/Animals Animals - Earth Scenes; I: M. &
C. Denis-Huot/Peter Arnold, Inc.; 2: David A. Northcott/Corbis; 3: M. & C.
Denis-Huot/Peter Arnold, Inc.; 4: Corbis; 5: Stan Westfall/AGE Fotostock;
6: Ruth Cole/Animals Animals - Earth Scenes; 7: John Foster/Masterfile;
8: Jeff Foott/Picture Quest.

▲ **Unit 5, Week 2** *We Can Fix It*
Cover, I: Richard Smith/Masterfile. 2: Steve Cole/Getty Images.
3: Brand X/Punchstock. 4, 5: G.K. & Vikki Hart/Getty Images. 6: Jeremy
Woodhouse/Masterfile. 7: Digitalvision/Superstock. 8: Eric Haugesag/
Milkshake Productions.

● **Unit 5 Week 2** *Animals and Their Babies*
Photo credits: Cover: Steve Bloom Images/Alamy; I: Stephen Krasemann/
Getty Images; 2: Steve Bloom Images/Alamy; 3: D. Robert Franz/Alamy;
4: Martin Rugner/AGE Fotostock; 5: Lenz/Picture Quest; 6: Jose Antonio
Jimenez/AGE Fotostock; 7: Stephen Krasemann/Getty Images; 8: W. Perry
Conway/Corbis.

▲ **Unit 6 Week I** *Hat, Cap, Hat*
Cover: Royalty-Free/Corbis. I: (t, r, b) Siede Preis/Getty Images;
(l) Royalty-Free/Corbis. 2: (t) David Young-Wolff/PhotoEdit; (b) Siede Preis/
Getty Images. 3: (t) Mark E. Gibson/CORBIS; (b) Royalty-Free/CORBIS.
4: (t) Paul Thomas/Getty Images; (b) Siede Preis/Getty Images. 5: (t) ©
Digital Vision Ltd.; (b) Siede Preis/Getty Images. 6: (t) B and C Gillingham
/Index Stock; (b) Royalty-Free/Corbis. 7: (t, b) Paul A. Souders/CORBIS.
8: (t) Bob Krist/CORBIS; (b) Comstock Images/Alamy.

● **Unit 6 Week I** *Where are We?*
Photo credits: Cover: Kevin Fleming/Corbis; I: Ariel Skelley/Corbis;
2: Patrick Bennett/Corbis; 3: ACE Stock Limited/Alamy; 4: Ariel
Skelley/Corbis; 5: Kevin Fleming/Corbis; 6: Michael Newman/Photo Edit;
7: Michael Newman/Photo Edit; 8: Jeff Greenberg/Photo Edit.

▲ **Unit 6, Week 2** *Rod Can See It*
Cover: Will Hart/Photo Edit. 2: Gabe Palmer/CORBIS. 3: Tony Freeman/
Photo Edit. 4: Turbo/Masterfile. 5: Jeff Greenberg/Photo Edit. 6: Reuters/
CORBIS. 7: Sky Bonillo/Photo Edit. 8: Michael Newman/Photo Edit.

● **Unit 7 Week I** *What Can You Do?*
Photo credits: Cover: Peter Griffith/Masterfile; I: Rommel/Masterfile;
2: Masterfile; 3: Comstock Images/Alamy; 4: PhotoLink/Getty Images;
5: Peter Griffith/Masterfile; 6: Getty Images; 7: Rommel/Masterfile;
8: Getty Images.

▲ **Unit 7, Week 2** *Hot Ben, Hot Lin*
Cover, 1–2: M Nader/Getty Images. 3: Dex Image/Getty Images.
4, 5: Ryan McVay/Getty Images. 6, 7: Steve Mason/Getty Images.
8: (l, r) H. Benser/Masterfile.

● **Unit 8 Week 2** *From Seed to Plant*
Photo credits: Cover: Getty Images; I: Michelle Garrett/Corbis; 2: Corbis;
3: Jim Sugar/Corbis; 4: Michelle Garrett/Corbis; 5: Photodisc Green/Getty
Images; 6: Getty Images; 7: Wally Eberhart/Getty Images; 8: Juan Silva/
Getty Images.

▲ **Unit 9, Week I** *Bug in a Web*
Cover, I: Darrell Gulin/CORBIS. 2: Layne Kennedy/CORBIS. 3: (t) Michael
Newman/PhotoEdit; (inset) Darlyne A Murawski/Getty Images. 4: Frank
Siteman/PhotoEdit. 5: David Crausby/Alamy. 6: (t) David Muscroft/Age
footstock; (inset) Photodisc/Getty Images. 7: Christina Kennedy/Alamy.
8: Michael Newman/PhotoEdit.

● **Unit 9 Week I** *Insects*
Photo credits: Cover: Getty Images; I: Getty Images; 2: (l) Getty Images;
(r) Getty Images; 3: (l) Getty Images; (r) Michael Newman/Photo Edit;
4: Michael Pole/Corbis; (inset) Getty Images; 5: (l) Ray Coleman/Photo
Researchers; (r) Getty Images; 6: (l) Getty Images; (r) G. Mermet/Peter
Arnold, Inc.; 7: (tl): George B. Diebold/Corbis; (tr) Clive Druett/Papillo/
Corbis; (bl) The Image Bank/Getty Images; (br) Peter Weber/Getty Images;
8: Nigel J. Dennis/Corbis.

▲ **Unit 9, Week I** *A Vet Can Fix It!*
Cover: David Loh/Reuters/Corbis. I: Brent Stirton/GettyImages.
2: Patrick Frischknecht/Peter Arnold Inc. 3: Steve Kaufman/Corbis.
4: Brent Stirton/Getty Images. 5: Jeffrey L. Rotman/Peter Arnold, Inc.
6: Reuters/Miguel Vidal/CORBIS. 7: Chuck Savage/CORBIS.
8: Mary Kate Denny/PhotoEdit, Inc.

● **Unit 9 Week 2** *Down in the Ocean*
Photo credits: Cover: Stephen Fink/Corbis; I: Jeffrey L. Rotman/Corbis;
2: Julie Houck/Corbis; 3: Kennan Ward/Corbis; 4: Peter Pinockn/Picture
Quest; 5: Stephen Fink/Corbis; 6: Jeffrey L. Rotman/Corbis; 7: Georgette
Douwma/Picture Quest; 8: Stephen Fink/Corbis.

▲ **Unit 10, Week 2** *Zip? Zig? Zag? Yes*
Ken O'Donoghue

▲ Decodable Readers
● On-Level Books

© Macmillan/McGraw-Hill